Recreational Songs

Published by the

CHURCH OF JESUS CHRIST OF
LATTER-DAY SAINTS

Under the direction of the

GENERAL MUSIC COMMITTEE

Printed in United States of America
The Deseret News Press

PREFACE

The Church Music Committee has made an earnest effort to assemble in this volume songs suitable for every recreational function of the various organizations of the Church. The contents of the book are classified under the following headings: Patriotic Songs—Folk Songs—Christmas Songs—Songs of the Great Masters—Songs from the Operas of Sullivan and Gilbert—Favorite Old Songs—Songs Especially Arranged for Community Singing—Nonsense Songs—Songs for the Barbar Shop Quartet—Pioneer Songs—and M.I.A. Songs.

The committee takes particular pride in the publication in this volume of several groups of choice folk songs of countries from which our Saints have emigrated. Grateful thanks go to the following persons who contributed these songs of their native lands and who assisted whenever necessary in translating them into English:

Wales .... John James

Spain .... Edward Balderas

Hawaii .... Zola McGhie

Sweden .... Tony Schrdall

Switzerland .... Margrit Lohner

Holland .... Frank I. Kooyman

Czechoslovakia .... Olga Miller

Russian Round .... Ray Halverson

Germany .... Alexander Schreiner

Denmark .... Ella Gale

Grateful acknowledgement is also extended to Fred Wolters, Jr., for the illustrations.

The committee also calls the attention of the users of this collection to the fact that the art side of Community Singing may be fostered through the proper use of this book. Three factors contribute especially to this phase of the collection, namely: (1) a very choice selection of numbers, (2) many beautiful arrangements, (3) many new accompaniments. Music directors everywhere should welcome this book also for the many new songs it contains. These songs have been included both for their particular beauty and recreational value.

SUGGESTIONS FOR THE
USE OF THE BOOK

Community singing, although fundamentally a recreational function, will most surely degenerate and cease to be if there is not generated within it a genuine musical experience. It is to this end that every song in this Recreational Song Book has been chosen and arranged. If presented properly, the most seemingly trivial song in the book may be given a musical effect which will have cultural value. The chief objective in community singing is to create such an enjoyable musical experience for the participants that they will seek a repetition of that experience.

Following is a brief outline showing how the various sections of the book may be used:

Patriotic Songs

Everyone should join in the singing of our patriotic songs and should be induced to sing them with sincere patriotic fervcr.

Folk Songs

This section lends itself to many different treatments. In the first place everyone should learn, or be taught, these beautiful songs. Then, as a second suggestion, programs may be made up wherein national costumes are exhibired. Third, solo singers may sing certain of these songs in a community "Sing" or descant parts such as are found in such songs as "Allan Water." As a fourth suggestion, certain stanzas of songs such as "The Quest" may be sung by the men while others are to be sung by the women. Fifth, gestures and simple dramatic action may be introduced with the singing of some songs. Sixth, a special quartet or chorus may be organized to sing certain songs or certain parts of songs as a feature of a community "Sing." The hymns found at the end of some of the national song groups are folk hymns of these countries and may be used to inject a religious note into a community "Sing."

Negro Spirituals

The Negro spiritual is the miracle of all song. It is unique in form in that the chorus, or refrain, usually precedes the verse or stanza and its origin can only be traced to the frenzied emotion of religious exhuberance. The Negro spiritual was popularized by the Fiske Jubilee Singers in a campaign which took them all over the world to raise funds for a Negro school. The infectious melody and rhythm of these songs have made them an important part of our American Folk Song Literature. They should always be sung with extreme sincerity.

Western Songs

Many of the Western Folk Songs contain little but doggerel verse. We present in this section four of the better ones.

Christmas Songs

The joyous strains of the Christmas songs cannot be excelled in any groups of folk songs. We present in this section many which may be new.

All of these songs have been carefully harmonized and may be used by large groups or small groups or special choruses.

Master Composers

Nothing can tone up a commmunity "Sing" more than the inclusion of a song from the Master Composers. Those presented in this section are not difficult but are most beautiful and give opportunity for special interpretation.

Songs from the Operas of Gilbert and Sullivan

The team of "Gilbert and Sullivan" knows no counterpart in the field of collaborators. Each supplemented the other so fully that one without the other never did anything which was noteworthy. The opera airs of Sullivan and the ingenious verse of Gilbert are and have been bywords of English-speaking peoples throughout the world. Five out of the two hundred odd songs and choruses from this immortal team are herein presented. These songs are a welcome addition to any community song collection.

Old Songs

All compilers of community song books are confronted with the question as to which of our so-called "old songs" should be perpetuated. Our true heritage of popular song is found in these timeworn favorites. (We use the term popular song in the sense of songs which are familiar.) No practical volume in point of size could be made up which would contain all of the lovely songs of the past which should receive consideration. The list presented herewith is at best only representative. Sing these songs in a manner which will perpetuate their intrinsic beauty.

Songs Especially Arranged

To perform songs from this section a specially prepared soloist or group must be brought in as the music indicates.

Nonsense Songs

Wholesome fun is the objective to be attained when songs from this section are used in a community "Sing." Such songs as "O Soldier, Soldier," "The Deaf Woman's Courtship," "The Keys of Heaven," "O No, John," etc. may be dramatized with excellent effect. "Aerey, Aerey," may be presented with soloist singing the verses and the group singing the chorus. Gestures may be worked into many songs.

Barber Shop Harmonies

These songs are for the men of the group. They are so easy to read that all of the boys and men who have had any experience whatsoever in glee clubs can sing them on the "spot."

Pioneer Songs

The Pioneer Songs are of local significance. They may be used on appropriate occasions.

COMMUNITY SINGING

Community singing is a unified group expression which uses singing as a medium. The purpose, aims, results, and benefits are all self-contained. There is no audience as in a musical performance, and the enjoyment one may get out of community singing is entirely based on his own participation. An event or circumstance which brings people together, such as a group marching, a crowd of students at a school function, or some other self-acting assemblage, will often induce community singing without definite leadership. The spontaety of this type of singing cannot be equaled. But where the momentum of community singing has to be generated by a leader, one qualification of leadership must stand out above all others—enthusiasm. The leader must rouse his audience and keep it roused throughout the entire performance. He must have at his command enough devices to excite everyone to participate. All environmental conditions must be conducive to a wholehearted singing project. The piano must be in the right place. The conductor's platform must not be too close to the audience or too far away or too high or too low. Above all, the leader must present interesting music in an interesting way.

Scmeone has this to say of the community song leader: "He is the epitome of musical enthusiasm. He organizes people into singing groups at the least provocation. All emphasis in the singing is placed on wholehearted participation. Any community can become musically enthusiastic if it possesses enough musically enthusiastic leaders to keep it stirred up."

THE AMERICAN HYMN
(Speed Our Republic)

Words and Music by
MATTHIAS KELLER 1813-1890

f Maestoso

1. Speed our re-pub-lic, O Fa-ther on high! Lead us in path-ways of jus-tice and right; Rul-ers as well as the ruled, "One and all," Gir-dle with vir-tue the ar-mor of might! Hail! three times hail to our coun-try and flag!

2. Rise up, proud ea-gle, rise up to the clouds; Spread thy broad wings o'er this fair west-ern world! Fling from thy beak our dear ban-ner of old; Show that it still is for free-dom un-furl'd! Hail! three times hail to our coun-try and flag!

THE STAR-SPANGLED BANNER

FRANCIS SCOTT KEY   JOHN STAFFORD SMITH

1. Oh, say! can you see, by the dawn's ear-ly light What so
2. On the shore, dim-ly seen thro' the mists of the deep, Where the
3. Oh, thus be it ev-er when free men shall stand Be-

proud-ly we hailed at the twi-light's last gleam-ing? Whose broad
foe's haught-y host in dread si-lence re-pos-es, What is
tween their loved homes and the wars de-so-la-tion! Blest with

stripes and bright stars thro' the per-il-lous fight, O'er the ram-parts we
that which the breeze, o'er the tow-er-ing steep, As it fit-ful-ly
vic-t'ry and peace, may the heav'n res-cued land Praise the pow'r that hath

watch'd, were so gal-lant-ly stream-ing? And the rock-ets' red glare, the bombs
blows, half con-ceals, half dis-clos-es? Now it catch-es the gleam of the
made and pre-served us a na-tion! Then con-quer we must, when our

burst-ing in air, Gave proof thro' the night that our flag was still there.
morn-ing's first beam, In full glo-ry re-flect-ed now shines on the stream.
cause it is just, And this be our mot-to: "In God is our trust!"

The Star-Spangled Banner

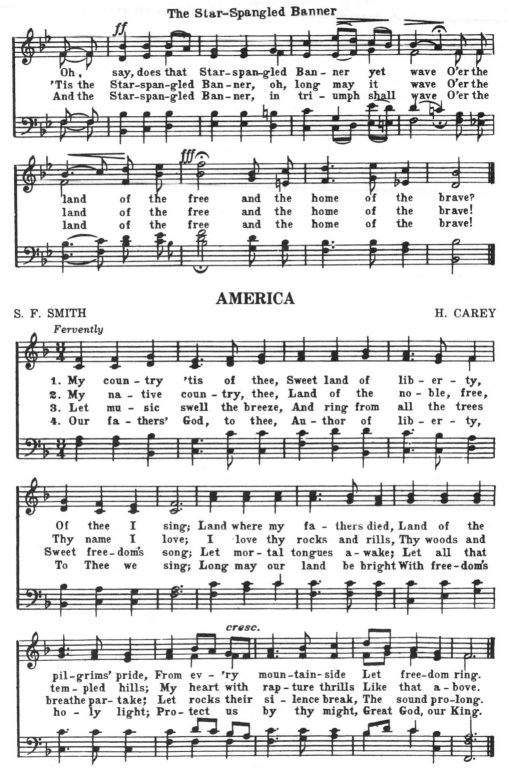

ff

Oh, say, does that Star-span-gled Ban-ner yet wave O'er the
'Tis the Star-span-gled Ban-ner, oh, long may it wave O'er the
And the Star-span-gled Ban-ner, in tri-umph shall wave O'er the

fff

land of the free and the home of the brave?
land of the free and the home of the brave!
land of the free and the home of the brave!

AMERICA

S. F. SMITH

H. CAREY

Fervently

1. My coun-try 'tis of thee, Sweet land of lib-er-ty,
2. My na-tive coun-try, thee, Land of the no-ble, free,
3. Let mu-sic swell the breeze, And ring from all the trees
4. Our fa-thers' God, to thee, Au-thor of lib-er-ty,

Of thee I sing; Land where my fa-thers died, Land of the
Thy name I love; I love thy rocks and rills, Thy woods and
Sweet free-dom's song; Let mor-tal tongues a-wake; Let all that
To Thee we sing; Long may our land be bright With free-dom's

cresc.

pil-grims' pride, From ev-'ry moun-tain-side Let free-dom ring.
tem-pled hills; My heart with rap-ture thrills Like that a-bove.
breathe par-take; Let rocks their si-lence break, The sound pro-long.
ho-ly light; Pro-tect us by thy might, Great God, our King.

9

BATTLE HYMN OF THE REPUBLIC

JULIA WARD HOWE

Air: "John Brown's Body"

Allegretto

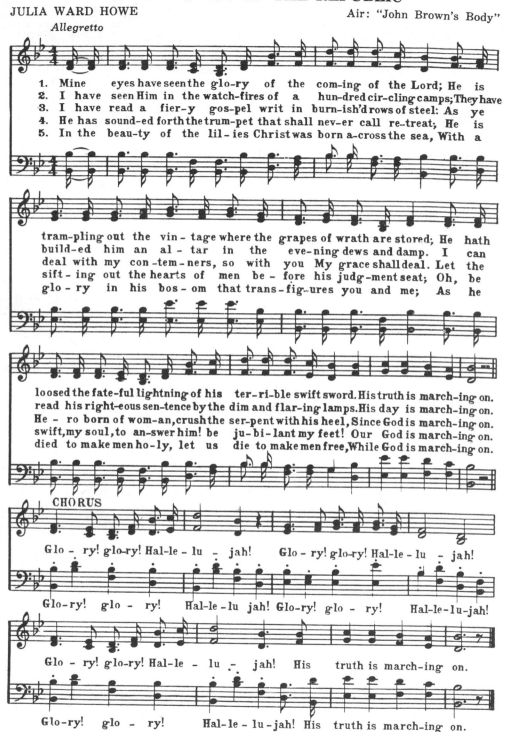

1. Mine eyes have seen the glo-ry of the com-ing of the Lord; He is
2. I have seen Him in the watch-fires of a hun-dred cir-cling camps; They have
3. I have read a fier-y gos-pel writ in burn-ish'd rows of steel: As ye
4. He has sound-ed forth the trum-pet that shall nev-er call re-treat; He is
5. In the beau-ty of the lil-ies Christ was born a-cross the sea, With a

tram-pling out the vin-tage where the grapes of wrath are stored; He hath
build-ed him an al-tar in the eve-ning dews and damp. I can
deal with my con-tem-ners, so with you My grace shall deal. Let the
sift-ing out the hearts of men be-fore his judg-ment seat; Oh, be
glo-ry in his bos-om that trans-fig-ures you and me; As he

loosed the fate-ful light-ning of his ter-ri-ble swift sword. His truth is march-ing on.
read his right-eous sen-tence by the dim and flar-ing lamps. His day is march-ing on.
He-ro born of wom-an, crush the ser-pent with his heel, Since God is march-ing on.
swift, my soul, to an-swer him! be ju-bi-lant my feet! Our God is march-ing on.
died to make men ho-ly, let us die to make men free, While God is march-ing on.

CHORUS

Glo-ry! glo-ry! Hal-le-lu-jah! Glo-ry! glo-ry! Hal-le-lu-jah!

Glo-ry! glo-ry! Hal-le-lu-jah! His truth is march-ing on.

10

YANKEE DOODLE

DR. SCHAMBURG

Old English Tune 1775

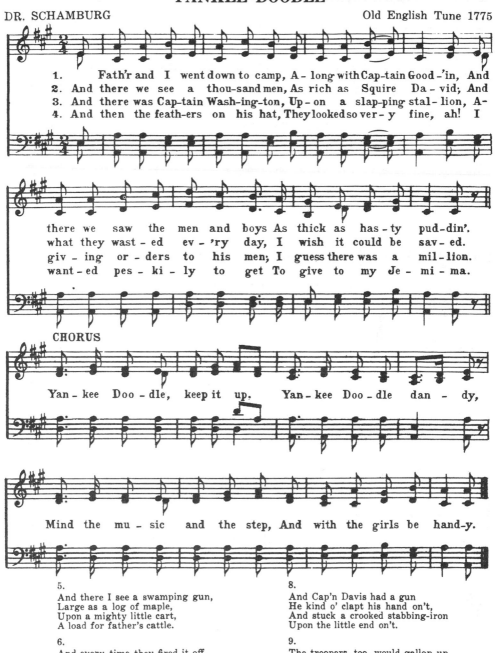

1. Fath'r and I went down to camp, A-long with Cap-tain Good-'in, And
2. And there we see a thou-sand men, As rich as Squire Da-vid; And
3. And there was Cap-tain Wash-ing-ton, Up-on a slap-ping stal-lion, A-
4. And then the feath-ers on his hat, They looked so ver-y fine, ah! I

there we saw the men and boys As thick as has-ty pud-din'.
what they wast-ed ev-'ry day, I wish it could be sav-ed.
giv-ing or-ders to his men; I guess there was a mil-lion.
want-ed pes-ki-ly to get To give to my Je-mi-ma.

CHORUS

Yan-kee Doo-dle, keep it up, Yan-kee Doo-dle dan-dy,

Mind the mu-sic and the step, And with the girls be hand-y.

5.
And there I see a swamping gun,
Large as a log of maple,
Upon a mighty little cart,
A load for father's cattle.

6.
And every time they fired it off,
It took a horn of powder;
It made a noise like father's gun,
Only a nation louder.

7.
And there I see a little keg,
Its head all made of leather;
They knocked upon't with little sticks
To call the folks together.

8.
And Cap'n Davis had a gun
He kind o' clapt his hand on't,
And stuck a crooked stabbing-iron
Upon the little end on't.

9.
The troopers, too, would gallop up
And fire right in our faces;
It scared me almost half to death
To see them run such races.

10.
It scared me so I hooked it off,
Nor stopped as I remember,
Nor turned about till I got home,
Locked up in mother's chamber.

COLUMBIA, THE GEM OF THE OCEAN

THOMAS A. BECKETT

Con spirito

Old English Tune

1. O Co - lum - bia, the gem of the o - cean, The home of the brave and the free, The shrine of each pa-triot's de- vo - tion, A world of - fers hom - age to thee! Thy man - dates make he - roes as - sem - ble, When Lib - er - ty's

2. When war wing'd its wide des - o - la - tion, And threat-en'd the land to de - form; The ark then of free-dom's foun- da - tion, Co - lum - bia, rode safe thro' the storm; With the gar - land of vic - t'ry a - round her, When so proud-ly she

3. The star - span-gled ban - ner bring hith - er; O'er Co- lum - bia's true sons- let it wave; May the wreaths they have won nev - er with - er, Nor its stars cease to shine on the brave. May the ser - vice u - nit - ed ne'er sev - er, But hold to their

Columbia, The Gem Of The Ocean

form stands in view; Thy ban-ners make tyr - an - ny trem-ble, When
bore her brave crew, With her flag proud-ly float-ing be - fore her, The
col - ors so true, The ar - my and na - vy for - ev - er! Three

borne by the red, white and blue. When borne by the red, white and
boast of the red, white and blue. The boast of the red, white and
cheers for the red, white and blue. Three cheers for the red, white and

blue, When borne by the red, white and blue, Thy ban - ners make
blue, The boast of the red, white and blue, With her flag proud - ly
blue, Three cheers for the red, white and blue, The ar - my and

tyr - an - ny trem-ble, When borne by the red, white and blue.
float-ing be - fore her, The boast of the red, white and blue.
na - vy for - ev - er! Three cheers for the red, white and blue.

GOD OF OUR FATHERS, WHOSE ALMIGHTY HAND

DANIEL C. ROBERTS

G. W. WARREN

Energetically ♩= 104

Trumpets

1. God of our fa - thers, Whose al - might - y
2. Thy love di - vine hath led us in the
3. From war's a - larms, from dead - ly pes - ti -

hand
past;
lence,

Leads forth in beau - ty all the star - ry
In this free land by thee our lot is
Be thy strong arm our ev - er sure de -

band
cast;
fence;

Of shin-ing worlds in splen - dor through the skies,
Be thou our Ru - ler, Guard-ian, Guide, and Stay,
Thy true re - lig - ion in our hearts in - crease,

Our grate - ful songs be - fore thy throne a - rise.
Thy word our law; thy paths our cho - sen way.
Thy bount-eous good - ness nour - ish us in peace.

BELLS OF FREEDOM
A FOUR PART ROUND

Bells of free-dom peal-ing loud and strong, wild and sweet the old fa-mil-iar song

Rhym-ing chim-ing roll - ing, toll-ing: bim, boom, bim, boom, bong.

FOLK SONGS

Many of the most delightful melodies in the world are of Folk Song origin. These songs are of corporate creation; no single person can be identified as having been solely responsible for any true Folk Song. This fact accounts for the simple beauty of the melodic lines of Folk Songs. They are easily remembered and are easy to sing because they contain no intricacies. To interpret them properly, one should use simple but sincere expression. The themes of the Folk Songs are the everyday experiences of the common folk. Rural life and pastoral life contribute more to the birth and preservation of Folk Songs than does urban life.

Great composers of music have used Folk Song melodies as thematic material in many, many compositions and ofttimes the Folk Song in such compositions has been used to crystalize nationalistic atmosphere. The basis of musical form is to be found in the simple Folk Song with its theme, repetition, contrast and restatement. The Folk Song is the most democratic of all music because it is the musical voice of the common people.

WALKING AT NIGHT

Czech

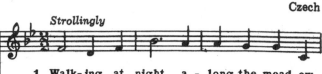

Strollingly

CZECHOSLOVAKIA

1. Walk-ing at night a - long the mead-ow
2. Near-ing the wood, we heard the night-in-
3. Man - y the stars that bright-ly shone a-

way, Home from the dance, be - side my maid - en
gale. Sweet - ly it help'd to tell my beg - ging
bove, But none so bright as her one word of

gay, Walk - ing at night a - long the mead - ow
tale. Near - ing the wood, we heard the night-in-
love. Man - y the stars that bright-ly shone a-

Walking At Night

way,   Home from the   dance, be - side   my maid-en   gay. Hey!
gale.   Sweet - ly   it   help'd to   tell   my beg-ging   tale. Hey!
bove,   But   none so   bright as   her   one word of   love. Hey!

Fast, as for dancing

Sto-do - la,   sto-do - la,   sto-do - la, pum - pa. Sto-do - la, pum - pa.

Sto - do - la,   pum - pa.   Sto - do - la,   sto - do - la,   sto - do - la,

pum - pa.   Sto - do - la,   pum - pa,   pum - pum - pum.

* The sign (♩) indicates a merry shout anticipating the dance.

NOTE: "Stodola" ordinarily means "barn" and "pumpa" a "pump." But in this song these words, though perhaps suggested by surroundings, are said to be merely a means of indicating gay, dancing rhythm. The long tone may be sung by a few sopranos with "ah."

Used by permission of the National Recreation Association.

THE QUEST

Bohemian Folk Song

Mother 1. Why are you stand-ing out-side, young man? Come in and
John 2. I did not come here to rest my-self. I came to
Mother 3. John, dear, be care-ful and do not choose One who is
4. John, dear, be care-ful and do not choose One who can't

tell us your quest, And if you're
stand up and woo. Three charm - ing
proud to the core, For she would
smile or look bright, For she might

feel - ing a bit fa - tigued, Sit down and talk while you
daugh-ters I know you have. I wish to get one from
not take a step with you, Ev - en as far as the
scowl at you ev - 'ry day, From ear - ly morn - ing till

The Quest

rest.
you.
door.
night.

Tra, la, la, Tra, la, la, la, la, la,

la, la, la, Tra, la, la, Tra, la, la, la, la, la, la.

Tra, la, la, Tra, la, la, la, la, la, la, la, la,

Tra, la, la, Tra, la, la, la, la, la, la.

19

ANNIE DARLING

Czech Folk Song

With Spirit

ah ha ha   ah ha ha   ah ha ha

An - nie dar-ling, An-nie dar-ling, You are my
An - nie dar-ling, An-nie dar-ling, I'll ev - er

ah ha ah   ah ha ha   ah ha ha   ah ha ha

pret-ty lit-tle dear. An-nie dar-ling, An-nie dar-ling, Be ev-er near.
more with you a-bide. An-nie dar-ling, An-nie dar-ling, You'll be my bride.

I care not what peo-ple say to me; I'll al-ways come back to you..
I care not what peo-ple say to me; I'll al-ways come back to you.

rit. ah ha ha   ha

I care not what peo-ple say to me; My love is true.
I care not what peo-ple say to me; My love is true.

*Descant for a few Sopranos on 2nd Stanza.

I WANDERED MANY YEARS

Czech Folk Song

Plaintively

1. I wan-dered man-y years, wan - dered to and fro through out the land. I wan-dered man-y years o-ver moun-tain, sea, and sand. Looked I ev-er for a qui - et place Where un-self-ish love would e'er a- bound. But in the whole world 'round Per-fect love at home I found.

2. I wan-dered man-y years; man - y were the lands to see, I wan-dered man-y years, but my home's the place for me. No - where in the world so bright-ly shines the sun. Love and peace a bound for ev - 'ry- one. Years and years did I roam, I found peace on-ly at home.

'NEATH OUR WINDOW

Bohemian Folk Song

Somberly

1. 'Neath our win-dow, 'Neath our win-dow
2. 'Neath our win-dow, 'Neath our win-dow
3. 'Neath our win-dow, 'Neath our win-dow

Snow is on the ground. 'Neath our win-dow, 'Neath our win-dow
Ros - es sweet-ly grow. Tell me, dear one, why the tear-drops
Stands a syc-a-more. Tell me, dear one, Tell me, dear one,

All with frost is bound. Soon the sun-shine will come smil - ing,
from your blue eyes flow? Good is life, and good is liv - ing;
Who is at the door? None come ev - er here to see me;

'Neath Our Window

Snow and frost will soon be go-ing. From the well the
Life and love must each be giv-ing. No more must your
None come ev-er here to see me. None will ev-er

sweet fresh wa-ter Will a-gain be found.
heart be griev-ing; Dry your tears, my love.
be my lov-er, For I am so poor.

I ALONE, I ALONE

Allegro Moderato

Czech Folk Song

1. I a-lone, I a-lone Brid-le my own team of hors-es.
2. I a-lone, I a-lone Take my loved one with me rid-ing.
3. I a-lone, I a-lone Hitch my ox-en to the wa-gon.

23

I Alone, I Alone

I a - lone, I a - lone Put the sad - dle on my horse,
I a - lone, I a - lone Plow the fields and reap the grain,
I a - lone, I a - lone Hitch my ox - en to the cart,

Brid - le my own team of hors-es, Take my sweet-heart with me rid - ing.
Take my sweet-heart with me rid-ing, Plow the fields and reap the har-vest.
Hitch my hors - es to the car-riage Take my sweet-heart to the par - ty.

I a - lone, I a - lone Put the sad - dle on my horse.
I a - lone, I a - lone Plow the fields and reap the grain.
I a - lone, I a - lone Take my loved one in my arms.

COME YOU, HERE, LADDIE

Czech Folk Song

Come you, here, lad-die, When day doth break. You may a les-son from me now take. Up with the birds, then Wat-er my herds; then Off you go lead-ing My graz-ing sheep. Up with the

Work is done, lad-die; I'm gay and young. So I sing mer-'ly A hap-py song. But while I'm sing-ing, And while I'm work-ing, My thoughts are for you The whole day long. But while I

Come You, Here, Laddie

birds, then   Wat - er   my herds; then   Off you go   lead - ing   My
sings, dear,   And while   I   work, dear,   My thoughts are   for you   The

graz - ing   sheep. hey.
whole   day   long. hey.

OH, GONE IS HAPPINESS

Czech Folk Song

Oh, gone   is   hap - pi - ness; Gone are   my   love and joy.
Sun - shine   makes fields grow green; Sun - shine makes flowers a - wake.

Oh, Gone Is Happiness

Oh, gone is hap - pi - ness; My life is sad.
Sun-shine makes trees grow tall; Why must my heart break.

All that was bright and gay Wat - ers took far a - way.
Las - sie whose heart is young Yearns for the love of one;

Oh, gone is hap - pi - ness; Gone is my joy.
No peace or joy is found, When love is done.

SING PRAISE TO HIM

JOHANN J. SCHOTZ

From the Bohemian Brethren's
Song Book

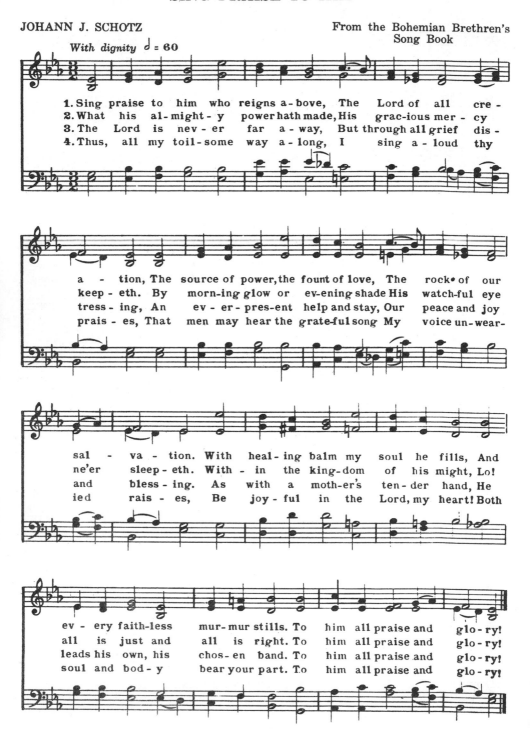

With dignity ♩ = 60

1. Sing praise to him who reigns a-bove, The Lord of all cre-
2. What his al-might-y power hath made, His grac-ious mer-cy
3. The Lord is nev-er far a-way, But through all grief dis-
4. Thus, all my toil-some way a-long, I sing a-loud thy

a - tion, The source of power, the fount of love, The rock of our
keep - eth. By morn-ing glow or ev-ening shade His watch-ful eye
tress - ing, An ev - er - pres-ent help and stay, Our peace and joy
prais - es, That men may hear the grate-ful song My voice un-wear-

sal - va - tion. With heal-ing balm my soul he fills, And
ne'er sleep - eth. With - in the king-dom of his might, Lo!
and bless - ing. As with a moth-er's ten - der hand, He
ied rais - es, Be joy - ful in the Lord, my heart! Both

ev - ery faith-less mur-mur stills. To him all praise and glo-ry!
all is just and all is right. To him all praise and glo-ry!
leads his own, his chos-en band. To him all praise and glo-ry!
soul and bod-y bear your part. To him all praise and glo-ry!

28

TWO LOVE-BIRDS

Danish Folk Song

DANISH

Andante con moto

Two lit - tle love - birds in a
Fare-well, fare - well, my tru - est

tree, So ve - ry sor - row-ful were they. Tho' friendship
friend, We nev - er - more will meet a - gain. Through all my

deep with - in the heart, The time had come for them to part. With grief her
life I'll think of thee, A friend in need, a friend in - deed. The for - est

lit - tle head she hung; He sang to her this part - ing song:
claims an emp - ty nest, For one flew East, the o - ther West.

ROSELIE

Danish Folk Song

In the gar-den with her moth-er, Sat Ros-e-lie dear; Of her
From the thick-et he had list-ened, Her heart to un-fold. Blushing

true love she con-fid-ed, But no one must hear.
cheeks were shy-ly hid-den From Pe-der so bold. He

laughed as he of-fered A small band of gold. Ha, ha,

ha, ho, ho, ho, ho, ha, ha, ha, ,ho, ho, ho, ho. She
ha, ho, ho, ho, ho, ha, ha, ha, ho, ho, ho, ho. He

Roselie

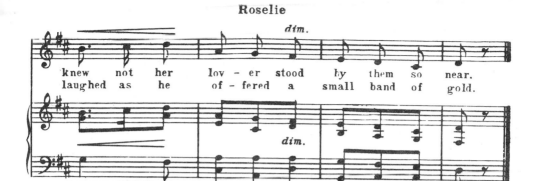

knew not her lov - er stood by them so near.
laughed as he of - fered a small band of gold.

SEE NOW WHO IS COMING HERE
or
"Danish Cavalier"

Danish Folk Song

See now who is com-ing here.'Tis no time to fear; he's a cav-a-lier.
I come from the king to you, With the sword and shield bringing right a-new,

He laughs at the en - e - my, and with en - er - gy, we will cheer. So
Fresh cour-age and man - ly will. I will hope in-stil in your heart. You

See Now, Who Is Coming Here

proud   and   shy,   the   la – dies smile as   he   goes   by; Bright
see,   I'm   here,   a   cav – a – lier with   pur – pose   clear; For

u – ni – form,   it   catch – es   ev – ry   eye.
you,   the   bat – tle   will   be   quick – ly   won.

CHORUS

mf–f

A   sold–ier brave who knows no fear, No   e–qual has a   cav–a–lier. His

cause is just;   In   God he trusts, Our coun–try's cav–a–lier.

DRINK TO ME ONLY
WITH THINE EYES

BEN JOHNSON   Old English Air

ENGLISH

1. Drink to me on-ly with thine eyes, And I will pledge with mine, Or leave a kiss with-in the cup, And I'll not ask for wine; The thirst that from the soul doth rise, Doth ask a drink di-vine; But might I of Jove's nec-tar sip, I would not change for thine.

2. I sent thee late a ro-sy wreath, Not so much hon-'ring thee As giv-ing it a hope that there It could not with-ered be; But thou there-on didst on-ly breathe, And sent'st it back to me; Since when it grows and smells, I swear, Not of it-self but thee.

WHEN LOVE IS KIND

When love is kind, cheer - ful, and free,

Love's sure to find wel - come from me.

But when love brings heart - ache and

When Love Is Kind

When Love Is Kind

When Love Is Kind

keep fond and true, through good re -
port, and e - vil to. Else here I
swear young love may go, for aught I
care, to Jer - i - cho!

37

WHICH IS THE PROPEREST DAY TO SING?

Con spirito ♩=92

DR. ARNE

Which is the prop-er-est day to sing? Sat-ur-day, Sun-day, Mon-day?

Which is the prop-er-est day to sing? Sat-ur-day, Sun-day, Mon-day?

Each, to be sure;'tis a migh-ty fine thing! Why should I name but one day?

Which Is The Properest Day To Sing?

Each, to be sure;'tis a migh-ty fine thing! Why should I name but one day?

Tell me your day; I'll tell my day; Let us but fix on some day.

Tell me your day; I'll tell my day; Let us but fix on some day.

Each, to be sure;'tis a migh-ty fine thing! Let us but fix on some day.

Which Is The Properest Day To Sing?

Tues - day, We'nes-day, Thurs - day, Fri - day, Sat - ur - day, Sun - day, Mon - day,

Tues - day, We'nes - day, Thurs-day, Fri - day, Sat-ur - day, Sun - day, Mon-day,

Which is the prop - er - est day to sing? Sat - ur - day, Sun - day, Mon - day,

rit. 2nd time only - - - - - - - - - -

Tues - day, We'nes-day, Thurs - day, Fri - day, Sat - ur - day, Sun - day, Mon - day.

THE NIGHTINGALE

From New Elementary Music by C. A. Fullerton.
Follett Publishing Company, Chicago.

English Folk Song

1. Pret-ty maid, come a-long; Don't you hear the fond song? The sweet
2. Pret-ty Bet-ty, don't fail, For I'll car-ry your pail, Safe-ly
3. Pri-thee sit your-self down With me on the ground, On the

note of the night-in-gale flow. Don't you hear the fond tale
home to your cot as we go. You shall hear the fond tale
bank where the prim-ros-es grow. You shall hear the fond tale

Of the sweet night-in-gale, As she sings in the val-ley be-low, — —

— — — — — — — As she sings in the val-ley be-low.

COME, LASSES AND LADS

Lively ♩=108

English Air, 17th Century

Come, lass-es and lads, Get leave of your dads, And a--

way to the May - pole hie, For ev - 'ry fair Has a

sweet - heart there, And the fid - dler's stand - ing by; For

Come, Lasses And Lads

Wil - ly shall dance with Jane, And John - ny has got his Joan, To trip it, trip it, trip it, trip it, Trip it up and down,

CHORUS

To trip it, trip it, trip it, trip it. Trip it up and down.

43

OH! DEAR! WHAT CAN THE MATTER BE?

Old English Song

Oh, dear! what can the mat-ter be? Dear! dear! what can the mat-ter be? Oh, dear! what can the mat-ter be? John-ny's so long at the fair.

1. He prom-ised to buy me a trin-ket to please me, And
2. He prom-ised to bring me a bas-ket of po-sies, A

Oh, Dear! What Can The Matter Be?

Oh, Dear! What Can The Matter Be?

Dal 𝄋

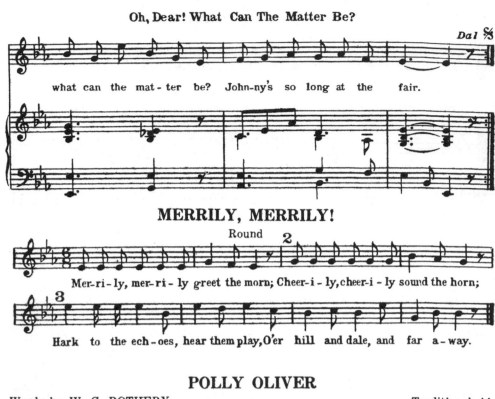

what can the mat-ter be? John-ny's so long at the fair.

MERRILY, MERRILY!

Round

Mer-ri-ly, mer-ri-ly greet the morn; Cheer-i-ly, cheer-i-ly sound the horn;

Hark to the ech-oes, hear them play, O'er hill and dale, and far a-way.

POLLY OLIVER

Words by W. G. ROTHERY

Traditional Air

Moderato

1. O pret-ty Pol-ly Ol-i-ver, one hot sum-mer's day, To
2. Her bas-ket was hea-vy, so Pol-ly sat down, To
3. "Ah me," cried Pol-ly Ol-i-ver, "what now shall I do? My
4. From Bath came that morn-ing the earl, rid-ing by, And he
5. The day they were wed-ded, she made him a cake Of

Polly Oliver

Mil - ver - ton mar - ket was ta - king her way, With a
rest by the way - side a mile from the town. She
fa - ther will beat me till I'm black and blue; Kind
sprang from his stir - rup when he heard Pol - ly's cry. Her
eggs, cream and but - ter, for fond mem - 'ry's sake, And

bas - ket of but - ter and eggs by the score, And
fell fast a - sleep there, and woke with a scream, For her
pow - ers, be - friend me, and come to my aid, Take
sto - ry she told, when he said "On my life, O
ev - 'ry year af - ter she brought him the same, And

rall.   Dal %

cream from the dai - ry, a gal - lon or more.
bas - ket was sto - len and spilt was her cream.
pi - ty up - on me, un - for - tu - nate maid."
pret - ty Polly Ol - i - ver, I'll make you my wife."
that's how Bath - ol - i - vers have come by their name.

rall.

47

ON THE BANKS OF ALLAN WATER

Old English Song

On The Banks Of Allan Water

more. For the sum-mer grief had brought her, and the

all. For his bride a sol-dier sought her, and a
more. For the sum - mer grief had brought her, and the

sol - dier, false was he; the banks of Al - lan

win - ning tongue had he; On the banks of Al - lan
sol - dier false was he; On the banks of Al - lan

Wa - ter None so sad as she.

Wa - ter None so gay as she.
Wa - ter None so sad as she.

COUNTRY GARDENS

Lively, bright with vigor

English Folk Song

Gar - dens are bloom-ing; wood birds are sing-ing. The sun shines bright on all to-day! Hill-side and val - ley, for - est and wood-land, a - dorn them-selves with flowers so gay. Hear the lark a - trill - ing,

Country Gardens

hap-py lark a-trill - ing, charm-ing the soul with songs of joy. In the

hush of the eve-ning, see all are gay, danc-ing joy - ous - ly to a

round- e - lay! Smil-ing bright-ly, fac - es all a - glow, In the

dance they trip it too and fro; Maid - ens light - ly

Country Gardens

trip-ping here and there, with the spring-tide blos-soms in their hair;

Hear the mus - ic play - ing, hap - py voic - es say - ing,

Come to the green and dance to - day to the sound of the pipes that

nim - ble fing - ers play; Come dance the hap - py hours a - way.

SUMMER IS A COMING IN
Summer Is Icumen In

Old English   13th Century English Round

Very Merrily

Sum-mer is a-com-ing in, Loud-ly sing cuck-oo!
Sum-er is i-cum-en in, Lhu-de sing cuo-cu!

Grow-eth seed and blow-eth mead, And springeth wood a-new.
Grow-eth sed and blow-eth med, And springeth w-de nu.

Sing, cuck-oo! Ew-e bleat-eth af-ter lamb; Low'th af-ter calf the
Sing, cuc-cu! Aw-e ble-teth af-ter lombe, Lhouth after cal-ve

cow; Bul-lock starteth buck, too, verteth, Merry sing cuckoo! Cuck-oo,
cu; Bul-luc sterteth, bucke vert-eth, Murie sing cuc-cu, Cuc-cu,

cuck-oo! Well singst thou, cuck-oo, O cease thee nev-er now!
cuc-cu! Wel singes thu, cuo-cu, Ne swik thu na-ver nu!

1 BASSES

Sing, cuck-oo, now, Sing, cuck-oo!
Sing, cuc-cu, nu, Sing, cuc-cu!

"Sumer is icumen in" is believed to be the oldest example of part-music in existence. The original MS, transcribed by John of Fornsete, a Monk of the Monastery of Reading, about the year 1226, is now in the British Museum.

The 1st bass or "Pes," as it is called in the original, with the 2nd bass should be sung by two adult male voices. They form a constant bass to the other parts. These parts should not be sung by treble voices because the notes would be sounded an octave too high. The round is usually sung without the basses.

*verteth, seeks the green fern.

I WILL SING A LULLABY

17th Century
English Cradle Song

Somewhat slowly

1. Gold - en slum-bers kiss your eyes; Smiles a wake you when you rise;
2. Care is heav - y, there for sleep; Moth - er here safe watch will keep;

Sleep, pret-ty lov'd ones; do not cry, And I will sing a
Sleep, pret-ty lov'd ones; do not cry, And I will sing a

lul-la-by,
lul-la-by, Lul-la-by, lul-la-by, lul - la - by.

NOW THE DAY IS OVER

SABINE BARING-GOULD

JOSEPH BARNBY

quietly

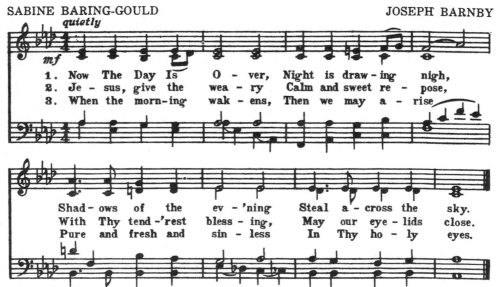

1. Now The Day Is O - ver, Night is draw-ing nigh,
2. Je - sus, give the wea - ry Calm and sweet re - pose,
3. When the morn-ing wak - ens, Then we may a - rise,

Shad - ows of the ev - 'ning Steal a - cross the sky.
With Thy tend -'rest bless - ing, May our eye - lids close.
Pure and fresh and sin - less In Thy ho - ly eyes.

CHRIST THE LORD IS RIS'N TODAY

CHARLES WESLEY

HENRY CAREY

With exaltation ♩ = 104

1. Christ the Lord is ris'n to-day
2. Love's re-deem-ing work is done,
3. Live a-gain our glo-rious King; Al - le - lu - ia!
4. Vain the stone, the watch, the seal;
5. Hail, the Lord of earth and heaven!

Sons of men and an-gels say,
Fought the fight, the vic-tory won.
Where, O death, is now thy sting? Al - le - lu - ia!
Christ hath burst the gates of hell!
Praise to Thee by both be given;

Raise your joys and tri-umphs high;
Je-sus' a-gon-y is o'er.
Once he died our souls to save; Al - le - lu - ia!
Death in vain for-bids His rise;
Thee we greet tri-umph-ant now;

Sing, ye heav'ns, and earth re-ply,
Dark-ness veils the earth no more.
Where thy vic-to-ry, O grave? Al - le - lu - ia!
Christ hath o-pened Par-a-dise.
Hail, the Res-ur-rec-tion Thou!

THE THREE CAPTAINS
French Folk Song

Translation by
GEORGE COOPER

Arr. by JULIEN TIERSOT

FRENCH

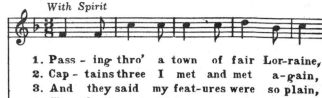

With Spirit

mf

1. Pass - ing thro' a town of fair Lor-raine,
2. Cap - tains three I met and met a-gain,
3. And they said my feat-ures were so plain,
4. Shoes don't count with beau-ty, I main-tain,

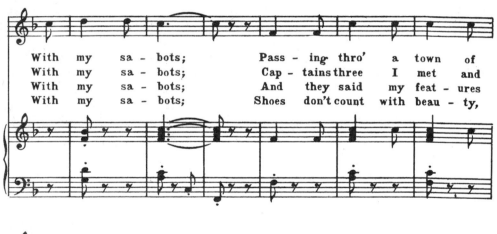

With my sa - bots; Pass - ing thro' a town of
With my sa - bots; Cap - tains three I met and
With my sa - bots; And they said my feat - ures
With my sa - bots; Shoes don't count with beau - ty,

fair Lor-raine, With my sa - bots, Cap - tains three I
met a - gain, With my sa - bots, And they said my
were so plain, With my sa - bots. Shoes don't count with
I main-tain, With my sa - bots; For the king's own

The Three Captains

met	and	met	a - gain,	With	my	sa - bots,	Don - dai - ne,
feat -	ures	were	so plain,	With	my	sa - bots,	Don - dai - ne,
beau -	ty,	I	main - tain,	With	my	sa - bots,	Don - dai - ne,
son	my	love	would gain,	With	my	sa - bots,	Don - dai - ne,

Oh!	Oh!	Oh!	With	my	sa -	bots.
Oh!	Oh!	Oh!	With	my	sa -	bots.
Oh!	Oh!	Oh!	With	my	sa -	bots.
Oh!	Oh!	Oh!	With	my	sa -	bots.

5. For the king's own son my love would gain,
   With my sabots, (repeat)
Gave me flowers which made me proud and vain,
   With my sabots;
Don-dai-ne, Oh! Oh! Oh!
   With my sabots.

6. Gave me flowers which made me proud and vain,
   With my sabots; (repeat)
Should they bloom, a royal queen I'll reign!
   With my sabots;
Don-dai-ne, Oh! Oh! Oh!
   With my sabots.

7. Should they bloom, a royal queen I'll reign!
   With my sabots; (repeat)
Should they fade, my own self I'll remain!
   With my sabots;
Don-dai-ne, Oh! Oh! Oh!
   With my sabots.

Permission granted by Harriett Cartwright from "Song Treasury."

IN THE SILVER MOONLIGHT

French Folk Song

Moderato

1. In the sil - ver moon - light, My good friend Pier - rot,
2. Thro' the sil - ver moon - light, Pier - rot makes re - ply.

Let me take your pen; I'd write a word or so;
I've no pen to lend you; Gone to bed am I,

Burn'd out is my can - dle; Fire I have no more;
In my neigh - bor's kitch - en, Some - one is a - stir;

As you wish God's mer - cy, Op - en now your door.
And her fire is burn - ing; Get a pen from her.

LORD, DISMISS US WITH THY BLESSING

WALTER SHIRLEY   JEAN JACQUES ROUSSEAU

1. Lord, dis-miss us with thy bless-ing; Fill our hearts with joy and peace;
2. Thanks we give, and ad-o-ra-tion, For the gos-pel's joy-ful sound;

Let us each, thy love pos-sess-ing, Tri-umph in re-deem-ing grace.
May the fruits of thy sal-va-tion In our hearts and lives a-bound.

O re-fresh us, O re-fresh us, Trav-'ling through this wil-der-ness,
Ev-er faith-ful, Ev-er faith-ful To the truth may we be found.

O re-fresh us, O re-fresh us, Trav-'ling through this wil-der-ness.
Ev-er faith-ful, Ev-er faith-ful To the truth may we be found.

ARE YOU SLEEPING?

French Version

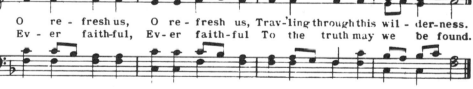

Fre-re Jac-ques, Fre-re Jac-ques, Dor-mez-vous, Dor-mez-vous?

Son-nez les mat-i-nes, son-nez les mat-i-nes; Din din don, din din, don.

MORNING, NOON AND NIGHT

CAROL CORNWALL

Moderato

1. The sun is out; the sky is blue. Where are
2. We'll run and play a-cross the lea. Come with
3. The night is come; the day is past, Home at

GERMAN

you? The fresh new grass shines bright with dew. Where are you? Lit-tle las-sies
me. We'll have such fun to-day, you'll see. Come with me. Gar-lands in your
last. The sum-mer days all go so fast; Home at last. Now that day is

gay with their lad - dies play, And they dance a-round-e-
hair and with - out a care, With a flaunt - ing
through, there is noth-ing more to do. Tar - ry not; it is

Morning Noon And Night

lay on this bright sum - mer day; But where are you?
air, nev - er one half so fair. So come with me.
true; home is wait - ing for you. It's home at last.

DOWN IN THE LOWER LAND

Moderato

1. Down in the low - er - land liv - ing is fine.
2. Man - y the hap - py hours ev - er are mine.

Hunt - ing is fash - ion there; Free - dom is ev - 'ry where.

Down in the low - er - land liv - ing is fine.

SPRING'S ARRIVAL

Tempo Ordinary

1. All the birds are here a - gain, All the birds to - geth - er.
2. O how hap - py are they all, Brisk and joy - ful danc - ing.
3. Their glad tid - ings giv'n to us Glad - ly we re - mem - ber.

What a won-d'rous ju - bi - lee, Twitt-'ring, tril-ling songs so free;
Lark and finch and blue - bird, too, With their friends all sing and coo,
Hap - py as their ju - bi - lee All of us will strive to be.

Spring now en - ters in with glee, Comes with joy - ous warb-ling.
Wish - ing hap - pi - ness to you, Bliss and joy for - ev - er.
Gay as all the birds shall we Sing and dance to - geth - er.

GOOD NIGHT

1.
Good night to you all, and sweet be thy sleep; May an - gels a-

2.

3.
round you their si - lent watch keep, Good night, good-night, good-night, good night.

TRUE LOVE

With Expression

1. {Num-ber all the stars that gleam there In the dark blue vault of heav'n;
    Num-ber all the lambs that wan - der In the mea - dow, hill, and glen.
Num-ber all the birds that twit - ter, All that hith - er thith-er flit - ter.
Put these num - bers all in one; They're my greet - ings, dear - est one.

2. {As I wan-der far to strange lands Should I see my love no more,
    Des-ti - ny, thy strong and cruel hand, Hide it from me, I im - plore.
Had I died ere love so gen - tle Clothed my heart as with a man - tle,
Would it now no heart-ache bring; Would I feel no pain - ful sting.

A KISS

Sprightly

A kiss is such a cur-ious thing. It's nev-er un-der-
And what a po-et may ex-press In thou-sand words or

stood. You eat it not; you drink it not; and
more, A sing-le kiss can well con-fess the

yet it is so good, so good. You eat it not; you
love you have in store, in store. A sing-le kiss can

drink it not; and yet it is so good.
well con-fess the love you have in store.

THE TWO ROSES

WOLFGANG VON GOETHE

H. WERNER

Moderately slow

German

1. On a bank two ros-es fair, Wet with morn-ing show-ers,
2. This in leaves of white ar-ray'd, Not a speck to dim them;
3. Like her cheeks,the blush-ing ray Which thy bud en-clos-es;

Fill'd with dew, in fra-grance grew, As I, pen-sive, full of care,
So I find the spot-less mind Which a-dorns my spot-less maid,
Bright-er far than you they are; But her charms if I should say,

Gath-er'd two sweet flow-ers.
In-no-cen-ce's em-blem. Tell me, ros-es,
You'd be jeal-ous, ros-es.

tru-ly tell, If my fair one loves me well.

SUSY, LITTLE SUSY

Translation

Fast

Folk Song
Sung in "Hansel & Gretel"
HUMPERDINCK

1. Su - sy, lit - tle Su - sy, now what is the news? The geese are go - ing
2. Su - sy, lit - tle Su - sy, some pen - nies I pray, To buy a lit - tle

bare - foot be - cause they've no shoes. The cob - bler has leath - er, but
sup - per of su - gar and whey. I'll sell my nice bed and go

no last has he, So he can - not make them the shoes, don't you see?
sleep on the straw. Feath - ers will not tic - kle and mice will not gnaw.

COME AND ENJOY LIFE

Lively

Sing with each stanza

Come and en - joy life While still the lan - tern glows

Come And Enjoy Life

Fine

And pick the blos - som   Ere dies the rose.

It   is   so eas-y to fret and stew, To seek for thorns and find them, too, And
When shy   the na - ture hides in clouds And loud the thun-ders ring a-bout,   It
Who nur-tures hones-ty in his heart And love to neigh-bors does im-part Soon

D. C.

no - tice not   the vi - o - let That   blooms a - long the   way.
seems that when the storm is past, The sun   shines e'er more bright.
finds that in   his house will dwell Con-ten - ted-ness ev - er - more.

PRAISE TO THE LORD

JOACHINE NEANDER

From the German

Joyfully, with dignity ♩=100

1. Praise to the Lord, the Al-might-y, the King of cre-a-tion; O my soul, praise him, for he is thy health and sal-va-tion; Join the great throng, psal-ter-y, or-gan, and song, Sound-ing in glad ad-o-ra-tion.

2. Praise to the Lord! o-ver all things he glo-rious-ly reign-eth. Borne as on ea-gle-wings, safe-ly his Saints he sus-tain-eth. Hast thou not seen How all thou need-est hath been Grant-ed in what he or-dain-eth?

3. Praise to the Lord, who doth pros-per thy way and de-fend thee. Sure-ly his good-ness and mer-cy shall ev-er at-tend thee. Pon-der a-new What the Al-might-y can do, Who with his love doth be-friend thee.

Praise thou the Lord,
Who with marvelous wisdom hath made thee!
Decked thee with health,
And with loving hand guided and stayed thee;

How oft in grief
Hath not he brought thee relief,
Spreading his wings for to shade thee!

Praise to the Lord!
O let all that is in me adore him!
All that hath breath
Join with Abraham's seed to adore him!

Let the "Amen"
Sum all our praises again
Now as we worship before him.

SONG OF THE ISLANDS

Slowly and Smoothly

CHAS. E. KING

HAWAIIAN

1. Love-ly is Ha-wai-i,   the is-land of Ke-a - we,   A-dorned with bril - liant le - hu - a   and fra-grant mai - le   of   Pa - na - e - wa.

2. Grand is Ma - u - i   with Ha - le - a - ka - la,   And 'tis for thee a - lone   the beau-teous rose   will   e'er   be   bloom-ing.

ALOHA OE

Farewell to Thee

QUEEN LILIUOKALANI

1. Proud-ly swept the rain-cloud by the cliff, As on it glid-ed thro' the trees;
2. Thus sweet mem-o-ries come back to me, And bring re-mem-brance of the past;

trees;
past;

Still fol-low-ing with grief the Li-ko, The a-hi-hi le hua of the vale.
Dear-est one, yes, thou art mine a-lone; Our love for e-ter-ni-ty shall last.

Fare-well to thee, fare-well to thee, Thou charm-ing one who dwells a-mong the bow-ers; One fond em-brace be-

Aloha Oe

fore I now de part, Un - til we meet a - gain.

BEAUTIFUL KAHANA

MARY J. MONTANO

CHAS. E. KING

For - ev - er, I shall sing the prai - ses of Ka-ha-na's
Ka - la - hi - hi o - la un - ex - cell - ed In grand-eur

Beautiful Kahana

beau - ty un - sur - pass - ed. The fragrance of the beau - teous
stands for ev - er near thee, For thou art en-dow'd with spec - ial

moun - tains By the zeph-yrs to thee is wafted.
charms And fav-or'd with a place by the sea.

Humming

MY HEART'S CHOICE

ALICE EVERETT

Slowly

'Tis the rain that is fall-ing on the le-hu-a (le-hu-a) That de-

lights the birds of the for-est (the for-est) and to me a sweet mes-sage it's

a mes-sage

bring-ing, Tell-ing of my fond love who's wait-ing there. For

mes-sage bring-ing

thee my heart is ev-er pin-ing, My be-

ev-er pin-ing

lov-ed one whom I hold dear. When the ev'-ning shades are

hold dear

fall-ing (are fall-ing) and the morn-ing rays of dawn ap-pear.

LONDONDERRY AIR

Words by W. G. ROTHERY

Irish Air

IRISH

1. In Der-ry vale be-side the sing-ing
2. In Der-ry vale a mid the Foyle's dark

riv - er, So oft I strayed, ah, man - y years a -
wa - ters The sal-mon leap a - bove the surg-ing

go, And culled at morn the gold - en daf - fo -
weir; The sea - birds call; I still can hear them

Londonderry Air

dil - lies that came with Spring to set the world a - glow.
call - ing In night's long dreams of those so dear.

Oh, Der - ry vale my tho'ts are ev - er turn - ing To your broad
Oh, tar - rying years fly fast - er ev - er fast - er; I long to

stream and fair - y cir - cled lea. For your green isles my ex - iled
see the vale be - lov'd so well; I long to know that I am

dim.

D.S. 𝄋

heart is yearn - ing, So far a - way a - cross the sea.
not for - got - ten, And there at home in peace to dwell. *Fine*

dim.

BENDEMEER'S STREAM

Four-part Arrangement

THOMAS MOORE

Irish Folk Melody

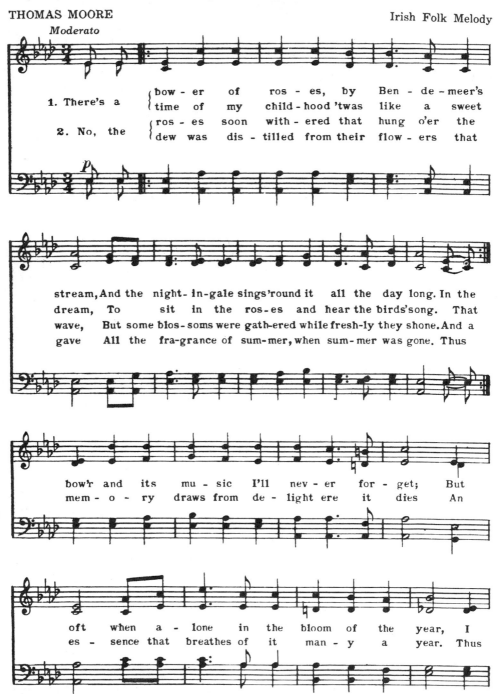

think, "Is the night-in-gale sing-ing there yet? Are the
bright to my soul, as 'twas then to my eyes, Is that

ros - es still bright by the calm Ben - de - meer?"
bow'r on the banks of the calm Ben - de - meer.

THE LOW-BACKED CAR

SAMUEL LOVER   Old Irish Air

Moderately fast

1. When first I saw sweet Peg-gy, 'Twas on a mar-ket day; A
2. In bat-tle's wild com-mo-tion, The proud and might-y Mars, With
3. Sweet Peg-gy round her car, sir, Has strings of ducks and geese, But the
4. I'd rath-er own that car, sir, With Peg-gy by my side, Than a

low-back'd car she drove, and sat Up - on a truss of hay; But
hos - tile scythes, de-mands his tithes Of death, in war-like cars; While
scores of hearts she slaugh-ters By far out-num-ber these; While
coach and four and gold ga-lore, And a la - dy for my bride; For the

The Low-Backed Car

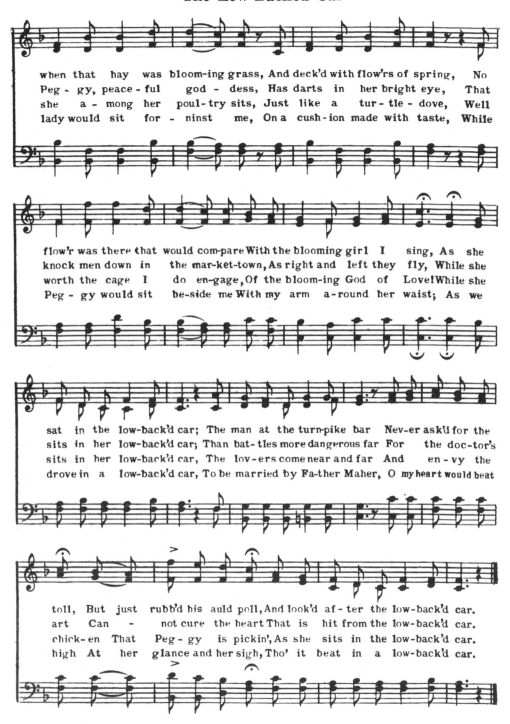

when that hay was bloom-ing grass, And deck'd with flow'rs of spring, No
Peg - gy, peace - ful god - dess, Has darts in her bright eye, That
she a - mong her poul-try sits, Just like a tur - tle - dove, Well
lady would sit for - ninst me, On a cush-ion made with taste, While

flow'r was there that would com-pare With the blooming girl I sing, As she
knock men down in the mar-ket-town, As right and left they fly, While she
worth the cage I do en-gage, Of the bloom-ing God of Love!While she
Peg - gy would sit be-side me With my arm a-round her waist; As we

sat in the low-back'd car; The man at the turn-pike bar Nev-er ask'd for the
sits in her low-back'd car; Than bat-tles more dangerous far For the doc-tor's
sits in her low-back'd car, The lov-ers come near and far And en-vy the
drove in a low-back'd car, To be married by Fa-ther Maher, O my heart would beat

toll, But just rubb'd his auld poll, And look'd af - ter the low-back'd car.
art Can - not cure the heart That is hit from the low-back'd car.
chick-en That Peg - gy is pickin', As she sits in the low-back'd car.
high At her glance and her sigh, Tho' it beat in a low-back'd car.

THE LAST ROSE OF SUMMER

THOMAS MOORE

Irish Air

Andante

1. 'Tis the last rose of sum-mer, Left bloom-ing a - lone;
2. I'll not leave thee, thou lone one, To pine on the stem;
3. So soon may I fol-low, When friend-ships de - cay,

All her love-ly com-pan-ions Are fad - ed and gone; No
Since the love-ly are sleep-ing, Go sleep thou with them; Thus
And from love's shin-ing cir-cle The gems drop a - way. When

flower of her kin-dred, No rose - bud is nigh, To re-
kind - ly I scat-ter Thy leaves o'er the bed Where thy
true hearts lie with-ered And fond ones have flown, Oh,

flect back her blush-es, Or give sigh for sigh.
mates of the gar-den Lie scent - less and dead.
who would in - hab-it This bleak world a - lone?

THE MINSTREL BOY

In march time

1. The min - strel boy to the war has gone; In the ranks of death you'll find him. His fath-er's sword he has gird - ed on, And his wild harp slung be - hind him. "Land of Song" said the war - rior bard, "Tho' all the world be - trays thee, One sword at least thy rights shall guard; One faith - ful harp shall praise thee!"

2. The min - strel fell! but the foe - man's chain Could not bring his proud soul un - der. The harp he lov'd ne'- er spoke a - gain, For he tore its chords a - sun - der. And said, "No chains shall sul - ly thee, Thou soul of love and bra - v'ry! Thy songs were made for the pure and free. They shall nev - er sound in slav - 'ry!"

BELIEVE ME, IF ALL THOSE ENDEARING YOUNG CHARMS

THOMAS MOORE   Air: "My Lodging Is In The Cold Ground"

Be - lieve me, if all those en - dear-ing young charms, Which I
It__ is not while beau - ty and youth are thine own, And thy

gaze on so fond-ly to - day,__ Were to change by to - mor-row, and
cheeks un-pro-faned by a tear,__ That the fer-vour and faith of a

fleet in my arms, Like__ fair - y gifts, fad - ing a -
soul can be known, To which time will but make thee more

way,__ Thou wouldst still be a - dored as this mo-ment thou art, Let thy
dear!__ No, the heart that has tru - ly loved nev - er for-gets, But as

love - li - ness fade as it will; And a - round the drear ru - in, each
tru - ly loves on to the close; As the sun-flow-er turns on her

wish of my heart Would en - twine it - self ver-dant - ly still!
god, when he sets, The same look which she turned when he rose.__

TIRITOMBA

MARBA JOSEPHSON

Italian Folk Song

Lively

1. Wake, the sun is bright-ly shin- ing o'er the moun- tain. Night is past, and morn- ing greets us. While the dew is on the grass-es, come go hik - ing To the sun-kissed hill - top high. Ti - ri - tom - ba, Ti - ri - tom - ba, Come now shed all care, and sor-row bid good-bye. Ti - ri - tom - ba, Ti - ri - tom - ba, We'll go hik - ing, you and I.

2. Now the trees and fields bright col-ors are dis - play - ing. Let us join in sport and laugh- ter. Sing-ing birds are dip-ping,wheel-ing, dart-ing, wing - ing, Joy-ous in the blue a - bove. Ti - ri - tom - ba, Ti - ri - tom - ba, Shar-ing na- ture's beau-ty, we can learn to play. Ti - ri - tom - ba, Ti - ri - tom - ba, We'll be care - free all the day.

Ti - ri - tom-ba Ti-ri-tom-ba Ti - ri - tom-ba Ti-ri-tom-ba

Ti - ri - tom-ba Ti-ri-tom-ba Ti - ri - tom-ba Ti - ri - tom-ba

MARIANINA

Italian Folk Song

Very gaily

1. Lit - tle Tus-can maid so gay and blithe, Love - ly as the land that
2. To the foun-tain in the vil - lage street She goes sing-ing in the
3. Soon she'll be my lov-ing bride, I know, Though I've nev - er real - ly

gave her life, Through the vine-yards and the ol - ive trees,
morn - ing sweet, And at eve - ning from the fields of green,
told her so; I must go a - way each Sat - ur - day,

Rings her laugh-ter on the breeze. Ma - ri - a - ni - na, tra - la
Sing - ing home-ward turns a - gain. Ma - ri - a - ni - na, tra - la
And to - day she bade me stay. Ma - ri - a - ni - na, tra - la

la, Ma - ri - a - ni - na tra - la - la, Ma - ri - a - ni - na, tra - la -
la, Ma - ri - a - ni - na tra - la - la, Ma - ri - a - ni - na, tra - la -
la, Ma - ri - a - ni - na tra - la - la, Ma - ri - a - ni - na, tra - la -

la, Ma - ri - a - ni - na, tra - la - la. O Ma - ria ni - na, O

Ma - ria - ni - na, No wild red rose was ev - er half so fair.

SANTA LUCIA

With swinging motion

Neapolitan Boat Song

1. Now neath the sil-ver moon O-cean is glow-ing; O'er the calm
2. When o'er thy wa-ters Light winds are play-ing, Thy spell can

bil-low Soft winds are blow-ing; Here balm-y breezes blow;
soothe us, All care al-lay-ing; To thee, sweet Na-po-li,

Pure joys in-vite us, And as we gent-ly row, All things de-light us.
What charms are giv-en, Where smiles cre-a-tion, Toil blest by heav-en.

Chorus

Hark, how the sail-or's cry Joy-ous-ly ech-oes nigh: San-ta Lu-

ci-a! San-ta Lu-ci-a, Home of fair po-e-sy, Realm of pure

har-mo-ny, San-ta Lu-ci-a! San-ta Lu-ci-a!

LA LUISELLA

Italian Folk Song

Joyously

1. Down in the love-ly mead - ow Close where the brook is run-ning, There
2. Here from my hill-top view - ing, I see my win some Mar - y, With

lives my blue-eyed Mar - y, Sing-ing the live-long day.
ac - cents soft and war - y, Sing I my roun-de - lay.

GLORY TO GOD ON HIGH

BODEN

FELICE GIARDINI

Praisingly ♩ = 92

1. Glo - ry to God on high! Let heav'n and earth re-ply;
2. Je - sus, our Lord and God, Bore sin's tre - men - dous load;
3. Let all the hosts a - bove Join in one song of love,

Praise ye his name. His love and grace a - dore, Who all our
Praise ye his name! Tell what his arm has done, What spoils from
Prais - ing his name; To him as - crib - ed be Hon - or and

sor - rows bore; Sing a - loud ev - er - more, Wor - thy the Lamb!
death he won; Sing his great name a - lone, Wor - thy the Lamb!
maj - est - y Through all e - ter - ni - ty: Wor - thy the Lamb!

THE SMALLEST

DR. J. P. HEYE

NETHERLANDS

Not too fast

p

1. In peace-ful vale of pleas-ant green, where
2. And on the hill-top lone and high, where
3. In val-ley low, on moun-tain tall, I

tin - y flow - ers are sway - ing, a lit - tle wa - ter-
sturd - y trees are tow'r - ing, there storm-winds, swift, are
feel the Lord is near me; but choose, if I may

fall is seen, that keeps the blos - soms bright and clean, and
sweep - ing by; there light - ning flash - es light the sky, and
choose at all, my qui - et nook, my wa - ter - fall, and

86

The Smallest

with its drops is ev - en spray-ing the small - est, And
fell, with force that's o - ver-pow'r - ing the tall - est, And
al - ways long to be, sin-cere - ly, the small - est, And

with its drops is ev - en spray-ing the small - est.
fell, with force that's o - ver-pow'r-ing the tall - est.
al - ways long to be, sin-cere - ly, the small - est.

THE LITTLE DUSTMAN

Translation

Folk Song of the Netherlands
Arr. by JOHANNES BRAHMS

Softly

1. The flow-'rets all sleep sound - ly Be - neath the moon's bright ray; They
2. Now see, the lit-tle dust - man At the window shows his head And

The Little Dustman

nod their heads to - geth - er And dream the night a - way. The
looks for an - y chil - dren Who ought to be in bed; And

rust'- ling trees wave to and fro, And mur-mur soft and low.
as each wear - y one he spies, Throws dust in - to his eyes.

Sleep on, sleep on, Sleep on, my lit - tle one.
Sleep on, sleep on, Sleep on, my lit - tle one.

"The Little Dustman" was dignified by the great composer, Brahms, in that he chose it from the many, many folk songs from the Netherlands to give the above most beautiful accompaniment.

PRAYER OF THANKSGIVING

Netherlands Melody

We gath-er to-geth-er to ask the Lord's bless-ings. He chas-tens, and has-tens his will to make known; The wick-ed op-press-ing, cease them from dis-tress-ing; Sing prais-es to his name; He for-

Prayer Of Thanksgiving

Ladies voices

gets not his own. Be - side us to guide us, our God with us join-ing, Or -

dain - ing, main-tain - ing his king-dom di-vine. So from the be - gin-ning the

fight we were win-ning; Thou Lord was at our side; all glo-ry be thine.

All Voices

We

Prayer Of Thanksgiving

all do ex - tol thee, Thou Lead - er in bat - tle, and pray that thou
still our De - fend - er wilt be. Let Thy con - gre - ga - tion es -
cape trib - u - la - tion. Thy name be ev - er praised. O Lord, make us
free; Lord, make us free.

NORWEGIAN

THE CHALET GIRL'S SUNDAY

Andante Sostenuto

dolce

I gaze on the sun; it mounts in the skies; the

hour now for church-time is near_ing. Ah! would I were home, a-

The Chalet Girl's Sunday

mid all I prize, with folk on the high-way ap-pear-ing. As

soon as the sun lights up on its way, The notch in the moun-tain crest

yon-der, The bells ring be-low for wor-ship to-day, re-

mind - ing of pray'r all who wan - der.

VOLGA BOAT SONG

RUSSIAN

Expressively

Yo, heave, ho, yo, heave, ho,

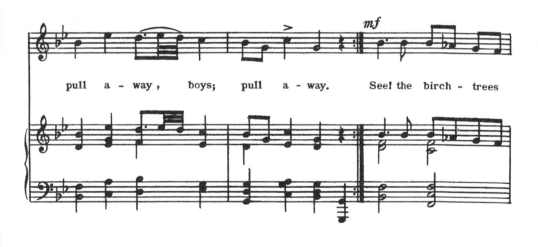

pull a - way, boys; pull a - way. See! the birch - trees

most in sight; Home we'll reach be - fore the night.

Volga Boat Song

Watch fires are burn-ing for our re-turn-ing. Home we'll reach be-fore the night.

D.C. (after D. C) *ppp*

Yo heave, ho, yo, heave ho.

To effectively sing this song, make a gradual crescendo to the middle phrase and then a gradual diminuendo to the final phrase.

RUSSIAN ROUND
(HI HO ROUND)
(2 or 4 part)

Vigorously

1 (1) **(2)**

Hi, ho! an-y-bo-dy home? eat or drink or mon-ey have I none,

2 (3) **(4)**

Still I will be hap - py. Hi, ho! an-y-bod-y home?

If low basses and tenors are available the following parts may be added to the round.

Contra Bass

Hi ho hi hi ho hi hi hi hi hi hi ho

Tenor

hi ho hi hi ho hi hi hi hi hi ho hi ho hi ho

hi ho hi hi ho hi ho hi ho hi ho hi hi ho.

HARK! THE EVENING HYMN IS STEALING

THOMAS MOORE

Russian Air

1. Hark! the even-ing hymn is steal-ing O'er the wa-ters soft and clear;
2. Now like moon-light waves re-treat-ing To the shore it dies a-long;

Near-er yet and near-er peal-ing, Soft it breaks up-on the ear.
Now like an-gry sur-ges meet-ing, Breaks the min-gled tide of song.

Sing ho-san-nah, sing ho-san-nah, sing ho-san-nah. A - men.
Sing ho-san-nah, sing ho-san-nah, sing ho-san-nah. A - men.

Far-ther now, now far-ther steal-ing, Soft it fades up-on the ear.
Hark! a-gain, like waves re-treat-ing, To the shore it dies a-long.

Sing ho-san-ah, Sing ho-san-ah, Sing ho-san-ah! A - men.

VERMELAND

Swedish Folk Song

Andante

Oh, Ver-me-land, all praise to the won-der-ful land, The bright-est of the jew-els of old Swed-en. No mat-ter where I roam, still my heart is true to you; My heart is yearn-ing ev-er for you, Swed-en, For there would I live al-way, and there will I stay, And there a maid-en fair gave to me her heart and hand. I know we will hap-py be in Ver-me-land.

LOCH LOMOND

ANON

Old Scotch Air
Arr. MARGARET C. RICHARDS

SCOTTISH

Andante

1. By yon bon-nie banks, And by yon bonnie braes, Where the
2. 'Twas then that we part-ed In yon shady glen, On the
3. The wee bir-dies sing, And the wild flowers spring, And in

sun shines bright on Loch Lo - mond, Where me and my true love Were
steep, steep side of Ben Lo - mond, Where in pur - ple hue The
sunshine the wa-ters are sleep-ing, But the brok - en heart it kens Nae

ev - 'er wont to gae, On the bon-nie, bon-nie banks of Loch Lo - mond.
high-land hills we view, And the moon com-ing out in the gloam - ing.
sec-ond spring a - gain, Tho' the wae-ful may cease frae their greet - ing.

CHORUS

Oh! ye'll take the high road, and I'll take the low road, And

Loch Lomond

I'll be in Scot-land a-fore ye; But me and my true love we'll

L.H.

Rit.- - - - -

nev-er meet a-gain On the bon-nie, bon-nie banks of Loch Lo - mond.

CHORUS *Harmonized for Mixed Voices*

Oh! ye'll take the high road, and I'll take the low road, And

I'll be in Scot-land a - fore ye; But me and my true love we'll

nev-er meet a-gain On the bon-nie, bon-nie banks of Loch Lo - mond.

OH, CHARLIE IS MY DARLING

Martial

SCOTCH

Oh Char-lie is my dar - ling, my dar - ling, my dar - ling!

Char - lie is my dar - ling; the young che - va - lier! 'Twas

on a Mon-day morn - ing Right ear - ly in the year, That
he came march-in' up the street, The pipes played loud and clear, And
hie - land bon-nets on their heads And clay-mores bright and clear, They

Char - lie came to our town The young che - va - lier.
a' the folks came run - nin' out To meet the che - va - lier.
cam' to fight for Scot-land's right, And the young che - va - lier.

Oh, Charlie Is My Darling

Oh, Char-lie is my dar-ling, my dar-ling, my dar-ling!

Char-lie is my dar-ling, the young che-va-lier!

fine

2. As
3. Wi'

COMIN' 'THRO' THE RYE

SCOTCH FOLK SONG

Moderately

1. If a bod-y meet a bod-y, Com-in' Thro' The Rye, If a-bod-y
2. If a bod-y meet a bod-y, Com-in' frae the town, If a-bod-y
3. A - many the train there is a swain I dear-ly love my-sel, But what's his name, or

CHORUS

kiss a bod-y need a bod-y cry?
greet a bod-y need a bod-y frown? Ev-'ry las-sie has her lad-die,
where's his hame, I din-na choose to tell.

Nane, they say, ha'e I; Yet a' the lads they smile on me, When Com-in' Thro' The Rye.

101

AULD LANG SYNE

ROBERT BURNS

Folk song

Andante

1. Should auld ac-quaint-ance be for-got, And nev-er brocht to mind? Should
2. We twa ha'e run a-boot the braes, And pu'd the gow-ans fine; But we've
3. We twa ha'e pai-dled i' the burn Frae morn-in' sun till dine; But
4. And here's a hand, my trust-y frien', And gie's a hand o' thine; We'll

auld ac-quaint-ance be for-got, And days of auld lang syne?
wan-dered mony a wear-y foot Sin' auld lang syne.
seas be-tween us braid has roared Sin' auld lang syne.
tak' a cup o' kind-ness yet For auld lang syne.

REFRAIN

For auld lang syne, my dear, For auld lang syne, We'll

tak' a cup o' kind-ness yet For auld lang syne.

HOW LOVELY IS THE EVENING

(THREE PART ROUND)

Allegretto

Oh, how love-ly is the evening, is the evening, When the bells are sweetly ringing, sweetly ringing, Ding, dong, ding, dong, ding, dong.

Oh, how lovely is the evening, is the evening, When the bells are sweetly ringing, sweetly ringing. Ding, dong, ding, dong, ding, dong.

ANNIE LAURIE

WILLIAM DOUGLAS

LADY JOHN SCOTT

Moderately quick

1. Max - wel-ton's braes are bon - nie, Where ear - ly fa's the dew,
2. Her brow is like the snow-drift; Her throat is like the swan;
3. Like dew on th' gow-an ly - ing Is th' fa' o'her fair - y feet,

And 'twas there that An - nie Lau - rie Gave me her prom - ise true,
Her face it is the fair - est That e'er the sun shone on,
And like winds in sum - mer sigh - ing, Her voice is low and sweet;

Gave me her prom - ise true, Which ne'er for - got will be; And for
That e'er the sun shone on; And dark blue is her e'e; And for
Her voice is low and sweet, And shes a' the world to me; And for

bon - nie An - nie Lau - rie I'd lay me doon and dee.
bon - nie An - nie Lau - rie I'd lay me doon and dee.
bon - nie An - nie Lau - rie I'd lay me doon and dee.

SCOTLAND'S BURNING
(ROUND)

1   2   3   4

Scotland's burning, Scotland's burning, Look out, look out! Fire, fire, fire fire! Pour on water, Pour on water!

COME LET US BE GAY

Hear how the mer-ry vi-o-lins gai-ly are play-ing. Young lads and pret-ty las-sies are danc-ing and sway-ing; List to the hap-py voi-ces their young hearts be-tray - ing. Now is the time for sing-ing; come, let us be gay.

SPANISH

JUANITA

CAROLINE NORTON   Spanish Melody

1. Soft o'er the foun-tain, Ling-'ring falls the south-ern moon;
2. When in thy dream-ing, Moons like these shall shine a-gain,

Far o'er the moun-tain, Breaks the day too soon! In thy dark eyes'
And day-light beam-ing, Prove thy dreams are vain, Wilt thou not, re-

splen-dor, Where the warm light loves to dwell, Wear-y looks, yet ten-der,
lent-ing, For thine ab-sent lov-er sigh? In thy heart con-sent-ing

Speak their fond fare-well. Ni-ta! Jua-ni-ta! Ask thy soul if
To a pray'r gone by? Ni-ta! Jua-ni-ta! Let me lin-ger

we should part! Ni-ta Jua-ni-ta! Lean thou on my heart!
by thy side! Ni-ta Jua-ni-ta! Be my own Fair Bride.

CIELITO LINDO

MARBA JOSEPHSON

SPANISH MELODY

1. Where moun-tains high Brace the blaz - ing sky Lives my
2. In wood - ed cove Ev - 'ry where we rove, Beau - ty

love-ly Cie - li - to Lin-do, Full of joy and bright
match-es Cie - li - to Lin-do, Flow-ers rare Mir- ror

laugh - ter, Friends and com-rades fol - low- ing af - ter.
feat-ures fair Of the love-ly Cie - li - to Lin-do.

Chorus

Ay, ay, ay, ay, Come, let's be

mer-ry. Let friend-ship grow; Keep the world a - glow.

Ciclito Lindo

Come to greet me, Cie - li - to Lin - do.

LA PALOMA
(The Dove)

SEBASTIAN YRADIER

1. The day that I left my home for the roll-ing sea, I
   And ere we sailed, I went a fond leave to take Of
2. And when I come home, from Nira to part no more, To
   A - dieu to the ship, a - dieu to the chang-ing sea; Then

said, "Moth-er, dear, oh, pray to thy God for me."
Ni - ra, who wept as if her poor heart would break.
rest with my moth - er dear on my na - tive shore;
home where with lov'd ones ev - er con-tent I'll be.

Ni - ra, if I should die, and o'er o - cean's foam
O - pen thy lat - tice dear-est, for it will be
Then comes the day, the hap-py and bless - ed day,
Ni - ra so fair all smiles will be at my side;

Some day a dove should flut-ter-ing to thee come,
My faith-ful soul that lov-ing comes back to thee.
Chas-ing all sad - ness, sor-row and care a - way;
Ni - ra so dear will be my own blush-ing bride.

La Paloma

CHORUS

Oh, a life on the sea, Sing-ing joy-ous and free, Ah,

we are go - ing, No one so gay as we! we!

COME, YE CHILDREN OF THE LORD

JAMES H. WALLIS   SPANISH MELODY

1. Come, ye chil-dren of the Lord, Let us sing with one ac-cord; Let us raise a
2. O how joy-ful it will be, When our Sav-iour we shall see! When in splen-dor
3. All ar-rayed in spot-less white, We will dwell 'mid truth and light; We will sing the

joy-ful strain, To our Lord who soon will reign On this earth when it shall be Cleansed from
He'll de-scend, Then all wick-ed-ness will end. O what songs we then will sing To our
song of praise, We will shout in joy-ous lays. Earth shall then be cleansed from sin, Ev-'ry

all in-iq-ui-ty; When all men from sin will cease, And will live in love and peace.
Sav-iour, Lord and King! O what love will then bear sway, When our fears shall flee a-way!
liv-ing thing there-in Shall in love and beau-ty dwell; Then with joy each heart will swell.

A SWISS WALKING SONG

SWISS

Allegro

1. From Lu - cerne to Weg - gis on,
2. O'er the moun - tain trail we'll go,
3. Weg - gis leads to the high - est hill;

Hol - di - ri - di - a, hol - di - ri - a, Care and la - bor now are gone,
Hol - di - ri - di - a, hol - di - ri - a, Love-ly deep ra - vine be - low,
Hol - di - ri - di - a, hol - di - ri - a, Give a cheer, girls, with a will,

REFRAIN

Hol - di - ri - di - a Hol-di - a,
Hol - di - ri - di - a Hol-di - a, Hol - di - ri - di - a,
Hol - di - ri - di - a Hol-di - a,

Hol - di - ri - di - a, Hol - di - ri - a, Hol - di -

ri - di - a, Hol - di - ri - di - a, hol - di - a!

109

IN EMMENTHAL

Moderato

Swiss Folk Song

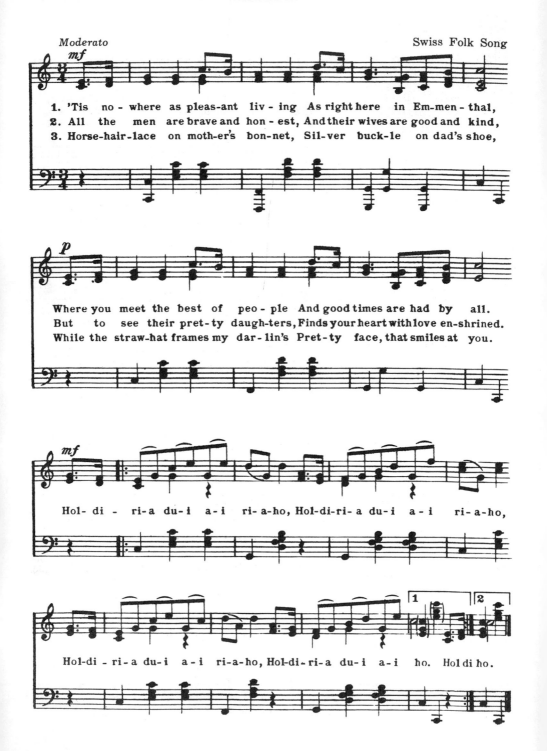

1. 'Tis no - where as pleas-ant liv - ing As right here in Em-men - thal,
2. All the men are brave and hon - est, And their wives are good and kind,
3. Horse-hair-lace on moth-er's bon-net, Sil-ver buck-le on dad's shoe,

Where you meet the best of peo - ple And good times are had by all.
But to see their pret-ty daugh-ters, Finds your heart with love en-shrined.
While the straw-hat frames my dar-lin's Pret-ty face, that smiles at you.

Hol- di - ri-a du-i a-i ri-a-ho, Hol-di-ri-a du-i a-i ri-a-ho,

Hol-di - ri-a du-i a-i ri-a-ho, Hol-di-ri-a du-i a-i ho. Hol di ho.

MY BAMBINA

Swiss Folk Song

Leggiero

Her pret-ty feet go tap-tap; Her pret-ty hands go
Hear man-do-li-nas play-ing And see gon-do-las

clap-clap. My dar-ling looks en-tranc-ing As gai-ly she is
sway-ing. Ca-mel-lias in her dark hair, Sweet per-fume scents the

danc-ing. While birds are blithe-ly sing-ing And
night air. As moon-beams soft-ly gleam-ing O'er

dis-tant bells are ring-ing, My sweet and dear bam-
star-lit wa-ters stream-ing, My own my sweet bam-

bi-na, I se-re-nade to you.
bi-na, I se-re-nade to you.

MARCH OF THE MEN OF HARLECH!

English Words by
JOHN OXENFORD

Welsh National Melody

With martial spirit throughout

WELSH

1. Men of Har - lech! in the hol - low,
'Tis the tramp of Sax - on foe - men,
2. Rock - y steeps and pass - es nar - row
Hurl the reel - ing horse-men o - ver!
3. Men of Har - lech! hon - or calls us,
Tho' our moth - ers may be weep - ing,

Do ye hear, like rush - ing bil - low, Wave on wave that,
Sax - on spear - men, Sax - on bow - men; Be they knights, or
Flash with spear and flight of ar - row; Who would think of
Let the earth dead foe - men cov - er! Fate of friend, of
No proud Sax - on e'er ap - pals us! On we march, what-
Tho' our sis - ters may be keep - ing, Watch for some who

surg - ing, fol - low Bat - tle's dis - tant sound?
hinds, or yeo - men, They shall bite the ground.
death or sor - row? Death is glo - ry now!
wife, of lov - er, Trem - bles on a blow!
e'er be - falls us, Nev - er shall we fly!
now are sleep - ing On the bat - tle - field!

Loose the folds a - sun - der, Flag we con - quer un - der!
Strands of life are riv - en; Blow for blow is giv - en;
For - ward, light - ly bound - ing, Hear the trump - et sound - ing!

March Of The Men Of Harlech!

Plac - id skies that hear our cries Shall launch their bolts in thun-der!
Dead - ly locks or bat - tle shocks When mer - cy shrieks to heav-en!
For - ward ev - er, back-ward nev - er, This proud foe a - stound-ing!

On - ward! 'tis our coun-try needs us! He is brav-est, he who leads us!
Men of Har - lech! young or hoar-y, See your ban-ner, Famed in sto - ry,
Fight for fa - ther, sis - ter, moth-er, Each is bound to each as broth-er;

Hon - or's self now proud-ly heeds us! Free-dom, God, and Right!
Strike for home, for life, for glo - ry! Nev - er will we yield!
With this faith in one an - oth - er We will win or die!

BELLS OF ABERDOVEY

Moderato

Bells Of Aberdovey

1. Maid-en come with me to dwell; If you love me, love me well, and
2. Come to me and plight thy troth; Wed-ded love shall crown us both, and

bind thy lov-er in a spell, say the bells of A - ber - do-vey
we shall tru - ly keep our oath, say the bells of A - ber - do-vey

One, two, three, four, I hear them play. Let

lov - er's hearts be blithe and gay, say the bells of A - ber - do-vey.

114

Bells Of Aberdovcy

Though the hills are green in May, and lit - tle birds are sing-ing,
Hear, my love, O do not chide, But soothe me in my ang-uish;

I pre - fer the mer - ry lay the tune - ful bells are ring-ing.
Prom-ise me to be my bride, and leave me not to lan-guish.

Maid- en, come with me to dwell; if you love me, love me well; And

bind thy lov - er in a spell, say the bells of A - ber - do - vey.

Bells Of Aberdovey

One, two, three, four, I hear them play. Let lov-er's hearts be blithe and gay, say the bells of A-ber-do-vey.

THE RISING OF THE LARK

Allegretto Moderato

The Rising Of The Lark

Hark! hark! the moun-tain lark has ris-en from the hea-ther dark, a-bove the gloom of night; New joys each note he sings, As he as-cends on buoy-ant wings, In ho-ly morn-ing light; There the new-born sun first found him, Ere did man on earth ex-ist.

Raise, then, thy trill-ing wings and leave be-low all earth-ly things, un-heed-ed and un-known! Soar far, yet thou art near, And tho' thy spir-it dwells not here, thy mus-ic show-ers down. Stars are pal-ing; day is break-ing Round the o-cean's burn-ing rim;

The Rising Of The Lark

Streaks of sun-shine gleam a-round him, silv - 'ry clouds and gold-en mist; For
Thou, a tongue of heav'n art speak-ing, while its star-ry eyes grow dim; They

ev - er could I up - ward gaze, To love him and to list.
rise up - on a thous-and hills, Bright na-ture's ser - a - phim!

cresc.

f

f

8va

ALL THROUGH THE NIGHT

English Words
WALTER MAYNARD

Welsh Air

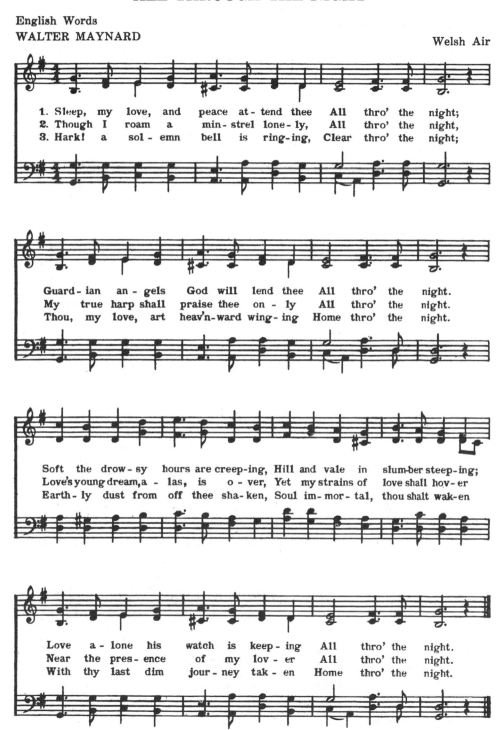

1. Sleep, my love, and peace at-tend thee All thro' the night;
2. Though I roam a min-strel lone-ly, All thro' the night,
3. Hark! a sol-emn bell is ring-ing, Clear thro' the night;

Guard-ian an-gels God will lend thee All thro' the night.
My true harp shall praise thee on-ly All thro' the night.
Thou, my love, art heav'n-ward wing-ing Home thro' the night.

Soft the drow-sy hours are creep-ing, Hill and vale in slum-ber steep-ing;
Love's young dream, a-las, is o-ver, Yet my strains of love shall hov-er
Earth-ly dust from off thee sha-ken, Soul im-mor-tal, thou shalt wak-en

Love a-lone his watch is keep-ing All thro' the night.
Near the pres-ence of my lov-er All thro' the night.
With thy last dim jour-ney tak-en Home thro' the night.

THE ASH GROVE

English Words by
THOS. OLIPHANT

Welsh Melody

1. Down yon-der green val-ley where stream-lets me-an-der, When twi-light is fad-ing, I pen-sive-ly rove; Or at the bright noon-tide, in sol-i-tude wan-der, A-mid the dark shades of the lone-ly Ash Grove; 'Twas there while the

2. Still glows the bright sun-shine o'er val-ley and moun-tain; Still war-bles the black-bird its note from the tree; Still trem-bles the moon-beam on stream-let and foun-tain, But what are the beau-ties of Na-ture to me? With sor-row, deep

The Ash Grove

black- bird was cheer - ful - ly sing - ing, I first met that
sor - row, my bos - om is la - den; All day I go

dear one, the joy of my heart! A - round us for
mourn - ing in search of my love! Ye e - choes! oh,

glad - ness the blue - bells were ring - ing; Ah!
tell me, where is the sweet maid - en? "She

then lit - tle thought I how soon we should part.
sleeps 'neath the green turf down by the Ash Grove."

GUIDE US, O THOU GREAT JEHOVAH
(CWM RHONDDA)

ROBERT ROBINSON

JOHN HUGHES

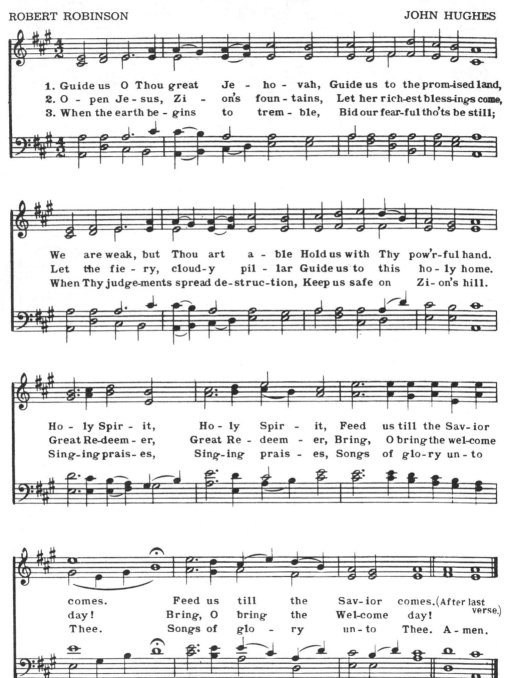

1. Guide us O Thou great Je - ho - vah, Guide us to the prom-ised land,
2. O - pen Je - sus, Zi - on's foun - tains, Let her rich-est bless-ings come,
3. When the earth be - gins to trem - ble, Bid our fear-ful tho'ts be still;

We are weak, but Thou art a - ble Hold us with Thy pow'r-ful hand.
Let the fie - ry, cloud-y pil - lar Guide us to this ho - ly home.
When Thy judge-ments spread de-struc-tion, Keep us safe on Zi - on's hill.

Ho - ly Spir - it, Ho - ly Spir - it, Feed us till the Sav - ior
Great Re-deem - er, Great Re - deem - er, Bring, O bring the wel-come
Sing-ing prais-es, Sing-ing prais - es, Songs of glo-ry un - to

comes. Feed us till the Sav-ior comes. (After last verse.)
day! Bring, O bring the Wel-come day!
Thee. Songs of glo - ry un - to Thee. A - men.

NEGRO SPIRITUALS

JACOB'S LADDER

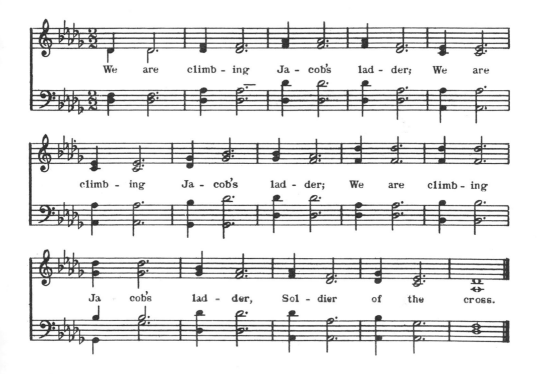

We are climb - ing Ja - cob's lad - der; We are climb - ing Ja - cob's lad - der; We are climb - ing Ja - cob's lad - der, Sol - dier of the cross.

Every round goes higher, higher,
    Soldier of the cross.

If you love Him, why not serve Him?
    Soldier of the cross.

Sinner, do you love my Jesus?
    Soldier of the cross.

Do you think I'd make a soldier?
    Soldier of the cross.

We are climbing higher, higher,
    Soldier of the cross.

From "Religious Folk-Song of the Negro," edited by R. Nathaniel Dett and published by the Hampton IInstitute Press.

SHORT 'NIN BREAD

Accompaniment by MARGARET C. RICHARDS

Negro Folk Song

Short 'nin Bread

Published by permission of Hampton Institute Press

NOBODY KNOWS THE TROUBLE I'VE HAD

Deep River

Deep, Riv-er, my home is o - ver Jor-dan. Deep,
Riv- er, Lord, I want to cross o - ver in - to camp-ground.

GO TELL IT ON THE MOUNTAIN

Go tell it on the moun-tain, O-ver the hills and ev - 'ry - where;

Fine

Go tell it on the moun - tain, That Je - sus Christ is aborn.

Solo

1. When I was a seek-er I sought both night and day, I
2. He made me a watch-man Up - on a cit - y wall, And

D.C.

ask the Lord to help me, An' He showed me the way.
if I am a Christ-ian I am the least of all.

HEAV'N, HEAV'N

(All God's Children)

American Negro Spiritual

JOSHUA FIT DE BATTLE OF JERICHO

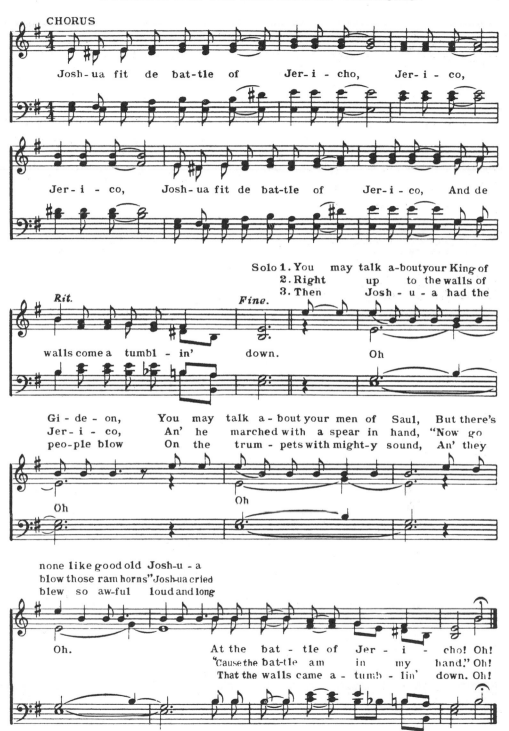

CHORUS

Josh-ua fit de bat-tle of Jer-i - cho, Jer-i - co,

Jer-i - co, Josh-ua fit de bat-tle of Jer-i - co, And de

walls come a tumbl - in' down. Oh

Solo 1. You may talk a-bout your King of
2. Right up to the walls of
3. Then Josh - u - a had the

Gi - de - on, You may talk a - bout your men of Saul, But there's
Jer - i - co, An' he marched with a spear in hand, "Now go
peo-ple blow On the trum - pets with might-y sound, An' they

Oh
Oh

none like good old Josh-u - a
blow those ram horns" Josh-ua cried
blew so aw-ful loud and long

Oh.

At the bat - tle of Jer - i - cho! Oh!
"Cause the bat-tle am in my hand." Oh!
That the walls came a - tumb - lin' down. Oh!

THERE IS A BALM IN GILEAD

CHORUS
Slowly

Negro Spiritual

There is a Balm in Gi-le-ad, To make the wound-ed whole, There is a Balm in Gi-le-ad, To heal the sin sick soul. There is a Balm in Gi-le-ad, To make the wound-ed whole, There is a Balm in Gi-le-ad, To heal the sin sick soul.

Fine
Solo

humming.........

1. Some times I feel dis-cour-aged and think my work's in vain, And then the Ho-ly Spir-it Re-vives my soul a-gain.
2. If you can-not sing like an-gels, If you can-not preach like Paul, You can tell the love of Je-sus, And say, "He died for all." *D.C.*

Oh

WESTERN

DOWN IN THE VALLEY

Flowingly

Down in the val - ley, the val - ley so low, Hang your head
Ros - es love sun - shine; vio-lets love dew; An - gels in
Build me a cas - tle for - ty feet high, So I may

ov - er; hear the wind blow. Hear the wind blow, dear; hear the wind
heav - en know I love you, Know I love you, dear, know I love
see her as she goes by, As she goes by, dear, as she goes

blow. Hang your head o - ver; hear the wind blow.
you. An - gels in heav - en, know I love you.
by. So I may see her as she goes by.

131

OLD CHISHOLM TRAIL

A fast Canter   Cowboy Song U.S.A

Now come a-long, boys, and lis-ten to my tale, And I'll
With a ten dol-lar horse and a for-ty dol-lar sad-dle I'm a-

tell you all my trou-bles on the old Chis-holm trail.
yell-in' and a-punch-in' those long-horn cat-tle.

Tenor or treble

Come - a ti - yi - yip - py yip - py
Melody

Basses I and II

Old Chisholm Trail

yay, yip-py yay; Come a ti - yi - yip-py yip-py yay.

3. It's cloudy in the West, an' a-lookin' like rain,
And o'course the old slicker's in the wagon again (Cho.)

4. It's bacon and beans 'most every day;
I wouldn't mind a change if it was prairie hay. (Cho.)

5. I went to the boss for to draw my roll;.
He had me figgered out nine dollars in the hole. (Cho.)

6. With my knees in the saddle and my hat in the sky,
I'll quit punchin' cows in the sweet bye and bye. (Cho.)

THE CURTAIN OF NIGHT

Cowboy Song

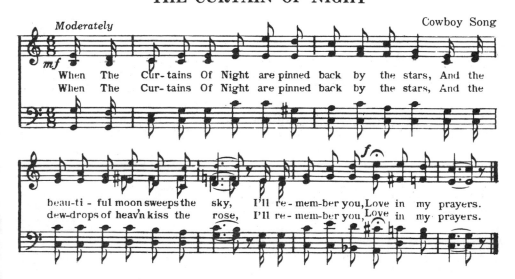

When The Cur-tains Of Night are pinned back by the stars, And the
When The Cur-tains Of Night are pinned back by the stars, And the

beau-ti - ful moon sweeps the sky, I'll re-mem-ber you, Love in my prayers.
dew-drops of heav'n kiss the rose, I'll re-mem-ber you, Love in my prayers.

HOME ON THE RANGE

Arr. by MARGARET C. RICHARDS

1. Oh, give me a home where the buf - fa - lo roam, Where the
2. How oft - en at night where the heav - ens are bright With the
3. Oh, give me a land where the bright dia - mond sand Flows lei -

deer and the an - te - lope play; Where sel - dom is heard a dis -
lights from the glit - ter - ing stars, Have I stood there a - mazed and
sure - ly down the stream, Where the grace - ful, white swan goes

cour - ag - ing word, And the skies are not cloud - y all day.
asked as I gazed If their glo - ry ex - ceeds that of ours.
glid - ing a - long Like a maid in a heav - en - ly dream.

Home On The Range

REFRAIN

Home, home on the range, Where the deer and the

an - te - lope play; Where sel - dom is heard a dis -

cour - ag - ing word, And the skies are not cloud - y all day.

Chorus harmonized for mixed voices

Home, home on the range, Where the deer and the an - te - lope play; Where

an-te-lope play

sel-dom is heard a dis- cour-ag-ing word, And the skies are not cloudy all day.

LO, SHEPHERDS, SLUMBER NOT

Czech Christmas Carol

Shep - herds, wake, slum - ber not; Wake ye, shep - herds; slum - ber not.

Haste ev - ery one to Beth - le - hem; Sil - ver stars shine in the sky;

An - gel's voic - es proud - ly cry, Je - sus Christ our Lord is born.

Lo, Shepherds, Slumber Not

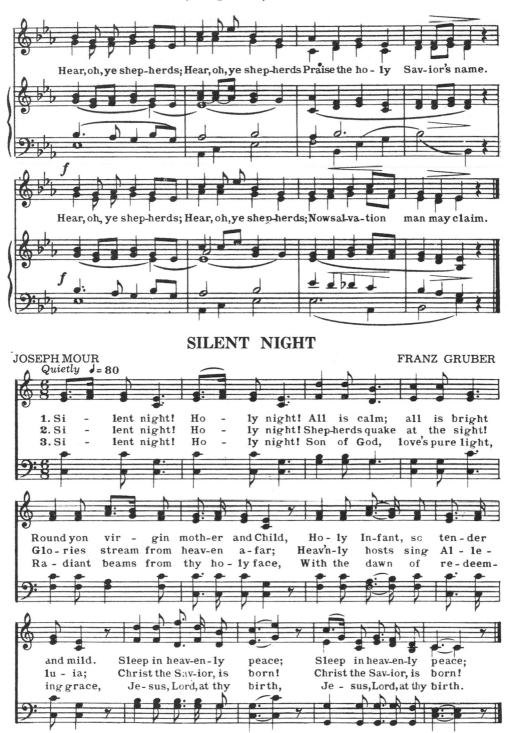

Hear, oh, ye shep-herds; Hear, oh, ye shep-herds Praise the ho-ly Sav-ior's name.

Hear, oh, ye shep-herds; Hear, oh, ye shep-herds; Now sal-va-tion man may claim.

SILENT NIGHT

JOSEPH MOUR

FRANZ GRUBER

Quietly ♩ = 80

1. Si - lent night! Ho - ly night! All is calm; all is bright
2. Si - lent night! Ho - ly night! Shep-herds quake at the sight!
3. Si - lent night! Ho - ly night! Son of God, love's pure light,

Round yon vir - gin moth-er and Child, Ho-ly In-fant, so ten-der
Glo-ries stream from heav-en a-far; Heav'n-ly hosts sing Al - le -
Ra-diant beams from thy ho-ly face, With the dawn of re-deem-

and mild. Sleep in heav-en-ly peace; Sleep in heav-en-ly peace;
lu - ia; Christ the Sav-ior, is born! Christ the Sav-ior, is born!
ing grace, Je - sus, Lord, at thy birth, Je - sus, Lord, at thy birth.

HALLELUJAH, HALLELUJAH

Joyously

Czech Christmas Carol

1. Hal - le - lu - jah, hal - le - lu - jah!
2. Hal - le - lu - jah, hal - le - lu - jah!

Let us be gay, for to - day Je - sus Christ is born.
Wel - come the lit - tle one; Sing un - to him our song;

Shep - herds and might - y bring Gifts to our Sav - ior King.
May you our Sav - ior Lord Love to us all re - ward.

Glo - ry and praise to the Sav - ior, the Al - might - y King.
Glo - ry and praise to the Sav - ior the, Al - might - y King.

GOD REST YOU MERRY GENTLEMEN

Traditional

Traditional English

Allegretto

1. God rest you mer-ry, gen-tle-men; Let noth-ing you dis may. Re-
2. In Beth-le-hem, in Jew - ry, This bless-ed Babe was born, And
3. From God our Heav'n-ly Fa - ther, A bless-ed an-gel came; And

mem-ber Christ our Sa - vi-or Was born on Christ-mas day, To
laid with-in a man - ger, Up - on this bless-ed morn; The
un - to cer-tain shep-herds Brought ti - dings of the same: How

save us all from Sa - tan's pow'r, When we were gone a - stray;
which his Moth - er Ma - ry, Did noth-ing take in scorn.
that in Beth - le - hem was born The Son of God by Name.

REFRAIN

O ti - dings of com - fort and joy, com - fort and

joy, O ti - dings of com - fort and joy.

ANGELS WE HAVE HEARD ON HIGH

Translated

Old French Melody

Allegretto

1. An - gels we have heard on high, Sweet-ly sing-ing o'er the plains;
2. Shep-herds, why this ju - bi - lee? Why your joy-ous songs pro-long?
3. Come to Beth - le - hem and see Him whose birth the an-gels sing;

And the moun-tains in re - ply Ech - o - ing their joy-ous strains.
What the glad-some tid - ings be Which in-spire your heav'n-ly song?
Come a - dore on bend - ed knee Christ, the Lord, our new-born King.

Glo - - - ri - a

in ex - cel - sis De - o, Glo - -

- - ri - a in ex - cel - sis De - o.

HARK, SHEPHERDS

Lively

Bohemian Christmas Carol

Hark, now, oh shep - herds, glad tid - ings we bring.
Hark - en, oh, shep - herds, now born is your King.

Beth' - lem brings to you a Sav - ior, and King.
Je - sus, the Sav - ior, brings joy to all men.

Hark and re - mem - ber: love one an - oth - er, Je - sus, our Sav - ior,

Born in a man - ger, Hal - le - lu - jah.

CANTIQUE DE NOËL
O Holy Night

ADOLPHE ADAM

Slowly and majestically

1. O ho-ly night! the stars are bright-ly shin - ing; It is the
2. Led by the light of faith se-rene-ly beam - ing, With glowing
3. Tru-ly he taught us to love one an-oth - er; His law is

night of the dear Sav-ior's birth; Long lay the
hearts by his cra-dle we stand; So led by
love, and his gos-pel is peace; Chains shall he

world in sin and er-ror pin - ing, Till he ap-
light of a star sweet-ly gleam - ing, Here came the
break, for the slave is our broth - er, And in his

Cantique De Noël

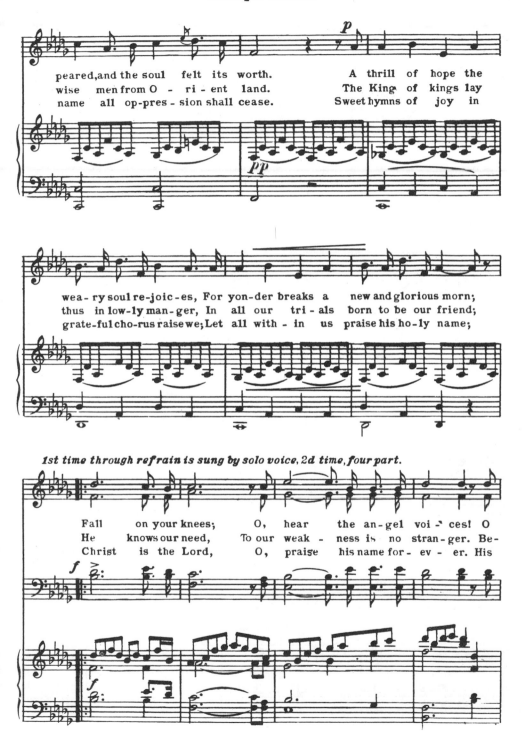

peared, and the soul felt its worth.
wise men from O - ri - ent land.
name all op-pres - sion shall cease.

A thrill of hope the
The King of kings lay
Sweet hymns of joy in

wea - ry soul re-joic - es, For yon-der breaks a new and glorious morn;
thus in low-ly man - ger, In all our tri - als born to be our friend;
grate-ful cho-rus raise we; Let all with - in us praise his ho-ly name;

1st time through refrain is sung by solo voice, 2d time, four part.

Fall on your knees; O, hear the an-gel voi - ces! O
He knows our need, To our weak - ness is no stran - ger. Be-
Christ is the Lord, O, praise his name for - ev - er. His

143

Cantique De Noël

night di - vine, O night when Christ was born! O
hold your King, be - fore him low - ly bend! Be-
pow'r and glo - ry ev - er-more pro - claim! His

night, O ho - ly night, O night di - vine!
hold your King, be - fore him low - ly bend!
pow'r and glo - ry ev - er-more pro - claim!

night, O ho - ly night, O night di - vine!
hold your King be - fore him low - ly bend!
pow'r and glo - ry ev - er-more pro - claim!

DECK THE HALL

Old Welsh Air

Joyously

1. { Deck the halls with boughs of hol - ly, Fa la la la la, la la la la.
    { 'Tis the sea - son to be jol - ly, Fa la la la la, la la la la.
2. { See the blaz - ing Yule be - fore us, Fa la la la la, la la la la.
    { Strike the harp and join the cho - rus, Fa la la la la, la la la la.
3. { Fast a - way the old year pass - es, Fa la la la la, la la la la.
    { Hail the new, ye lads and lass - es, Fa la la la la, la la la la.

Don we now our gay ap - par - rel, Fa la la la
Fol - low me in mer - ry meas - ure, Fa la la la
Sing we joy - ous all to - geth - er, Fa la la la

la la la; Troll the an - cient Yule-tide car - ol, Fa la la la la la
la la la, While I tell of Yule-tide trea-sure, Fa la la la la la
la la la, Heed-less of the wind and weath-er, Fa la la la la la

pp after last stanza

la la la.
la la la. Fa la la la la la la la la.
la la la.

145

LULLAY, THOU LITTLE TINY CHILD

Moderato

English Carol from Coventry

1. Lul - lay, Thou lit - tle, ti - ny child, By - by, lul - lay, lul -
2. O sis - ters two, how may we do, For to pre - serve this
3. Her - od the king, In his rag - ing, Charged he hath this
4. That woe is me, Poor child, for thee, And ev - er moan, and

f   *mf*

lay.   Lul - lay, thou lit - tle, ti - ny child,
day?   This poor young - ling for whom we sing,
day,   His men of might, In his own sight,
may,   May for thy part - ing nei - ther say or sing,

mp   1-2-3

By - by, lul - lay, lul - lay.
By - by, lul - lay, lul - lay.
All young chil - dren to slay.
By - by, lul - lay, lul - lay.

Used by Permission of Boston Music Co.

LOVELY EVENING

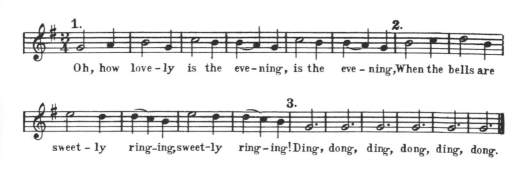

Oh, how love - ly is the eve - ning, is the eve - ning, When the bells are

sweet - ly ring - ing, sweet - ly ring - ing! Ding, dong, ding, dong, ding, dong.

JOLLY OLD SAINT NICHOLAS

Joyously

1. Jol - ly old Saint Ni - cho - las, Lean your ear this way!
2. When the clock is strik - ing twelve, When I'm fast a - sleep,
3. John - ny wants a pair of skates; Su - sy wants a dol - ly.

Don't you tell a sin - gle soul What I'm going to say;
Down the chim - ney broad and black, With your pack you'll creep;
Nel - lie wants a sto - ry - book; She thinks dolls are fol - ly.

Christ - mas Eve is com - ing soon; Now, you dear old man,
All the stock - ings you will find Hang - ing in a row;
As for me, my lit - tle brain Is - n't ver - y bright;

Whis - per what you'll bring to me; Tell me if you can.
Mine will be the short - est one, You'll be sure to know.
Choose for me, old San - ta Claus, What you think is right.

THE FIRST NOWELL

Words Traditional

Andante

Melody Traditional

1. The first Now - ell, the an - gel did say, Was to
2. They look - ed up and saw a star Shin - ing
3. This star drew nigh to the north - west, O'er
4. Then en - tered in those Wise Men three, Fell

cer - tain poor shep - herds in fields as they lay, In
in the East be - yond them far, And
Beth - le - hem it took its rest, And
rev - 'rent - ly up - on their knee, And

fields where they lay keep - ing their sheep On a
to the earth it gave great light, And
there it did both stop and stay Right
of - fer'd there in his pres - ence, Their

cold win - ter's night that was so deep.
so it con - tin - ued both day and night.
o - ver the place where Je - sus lay.
gold and myrrh and frank - in - cense.

The First Nowell

CHORUS

Sing Now - ell, Sing Now - ell,

Now - ell, Now - ell, Now - ell, Now - ell,

Sing Now - ell, Sing Now - ell.

Born is the King of Is - ra - el.

THE BELL IS RINGING
Round

Lively

1 Hark! the bell is ring-ing, Call-ing us to sing-ing, Hear the cheerful lay, Come, come, come away!

2 Hark! the bell is ring-ing, Call-ing us to sing-ing, Hear the cheerful lay, Come, come, come away!

3 Hark! Hark! the bell is ring-ing, Call-ing us to sing-ing, Come, come, come, come a-way!

149

GOOD KING WENCESLAS

JOHN M. NEAL

Traditional

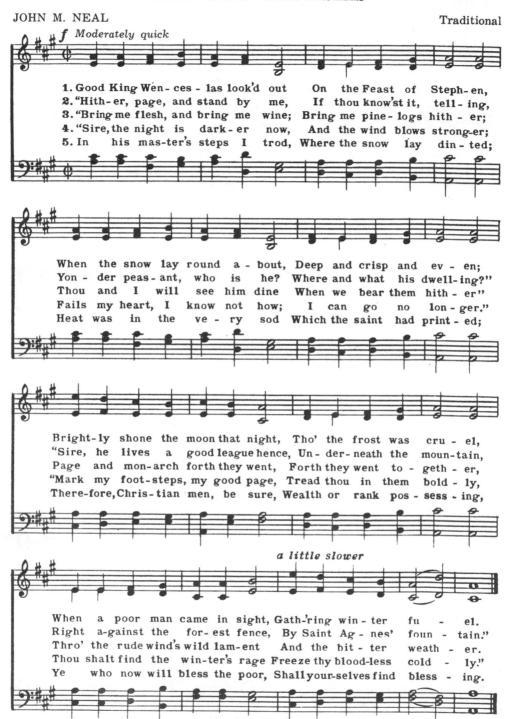

1. Good King Wen - ces - las look'd out   On the Feast of Steph - en,
2. "Hith- er, page, and stand by   me,   If thou know'st it, tell - ing,
3. "Bring me flesh, and bring me   wine; Bring me pine - logs hith - er;
4. "Sire, the night is dark - er   now,   And the wind blows strong-er;
5. In   his mas-ter's steps I   trod, Where the snow lay din - ted;

When the snow lay round a - bout, Deep and crisp and ev - en;
Yon - der peas - ant, who is   he? Where and what his dwell-ing?"
Thou and I will   see him dine When we bear them hith - er"
Fails my heart, I   know not how; I can go   no lon - ger."
Heat was in the ve - ry   sod Which the saint had print - ed;

Bright-ly shone the moon that night, Tho' the frost was   cru - el,
"Sire, he lives a good league hence, Un - der- neath the moun-tain,
Page and mon-arch forth they went, Forth they went to - geth - er,
"Mark my foot-steps, my good page, Tread thou in them bold - ly,
There-fore, Chris-tian men, be sure, Wealth or rank pos - sess - ing,

a little slower

When a poor man came in sight, Gath-'ring win - ter   fu - el.
Right a-gainst the   for - est fence, By Saint Ag - nes' foun - tain."
Thro' the rude wind's wild lam-ent And the bit - ter weath - er.
Thou shalt find the win-ter's rage Freeze thy blood-less cold - ly."
Ye   who now will bless the poor, Shall your-selves find bless - ing.

UP ON THE HOUSE-TOP

Allegretto

1. Up on the house-top the rein-deer pause; Out jumps good old
2. First comes the stock-ing of lit - tle Nell; Oh, dear San - ta,
3. Next comes the stock-ing of lit - tle Will; Oh, just see what a

San - ta Claus; Down thro' the chim - ney with lots of toys,
fill it well; Give her a dol - ly that laughs and cries,
glori - ous fill! Here are a ham - mer and lots of tacks,

CHORUS

All for the lit-tle ones, Christ-mas joys.
One that will open and shut her eyes. Ho, ho, ho! who would-n't go!
Al - so a ball and a whip that cracks.

Ho, ho, ho! who would - n't go! Up - on the house - top,

click, click, click, Down thro' the chimney with good Saint Nick.

O LITTLE TOWN OF BETHLEHEM

PHILLIPS BROOKS   LOUIS H. REDNER

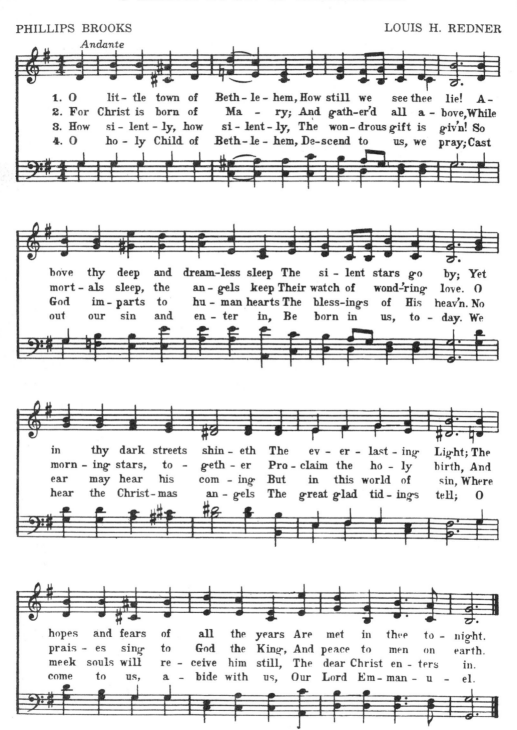

1. O lit-tle town of Beth-le-hem, How still we see thee lie! A-bove thy deep and dream-less sleep The si-lent stars go by; Yet in thy dark streets shin-eth The ev-er-last-ing Light; The hopes and fears of all the years Are met in thee to-night.

2. For Christ is born of Ma-ry; And gath-er'd all a-bove, While mort-als sleep, the an-gels keep Their watch of wond'ring love. O morn-ing stars, to-geth-er Pro-claim the ho-ly birth, And prais-es sing to God the King, And peace to men on earth.

3. How si-lent-ly, how si-lent-ly, The won-drous gift is giv'n! So God im-parts to hu-man hearts The bless-ings of His heav'n. No ear may hear his com-ing But in this world of sin, Where meek souls will re-ceive him still, The dear Christ en-ters in.

4. O ho-ly Child of Beth-le-hem, De-scend to us, we pray; Cast out our sin and en-ter in, Be born in us, to-day. We hear the Christ-mas an-gels The great glad tid-ings tell; O come to us, a-bide with us, Our Lord Em-man-u-el.

SHEPHERDS, SHAKE OFF YOUR DROWSY SLEEP

Semi-Chorus

Vivace

BESANCON CAROL

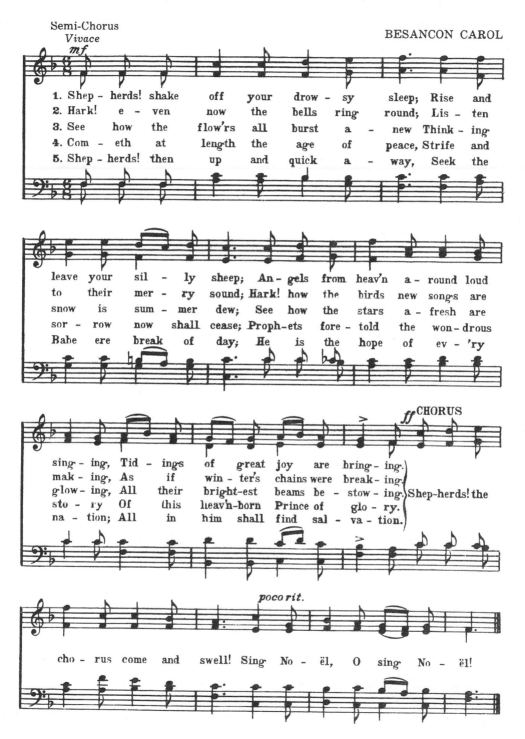

1. Shep - herds! shake off your drow - sy sleep; Rise and leave your sil - ly sheep; An - gels from heav'n a - round loud sing - ing, Tid - ings of great joy are bring - ing.

2. Hark! e - ven now the bells ring round; Lis - ten to their mer - ry sound; Hark! how the birds new songs are mak - ing, As if win - ter's chains were break - ing.

3. See how the flow'rs all burst a - new Think - ing snow is sum - mer dew; See how the stars a - fresh are glow - ing, All their bright-est beams be - stow - ing.

4. Com - eth at length the age of peace, Strife and sor - row now shall cease; Proph-ets fore - told the won - drous sto - ry Of this heav'n-born Prince of glo - ry.

5. Shep - herds! then up and quick a - way, Seek the Babe ere break of day; He is the hope of ev - 'ry na - tion; All in him shall find sal - va - tion.

ff CHORUS

Shep-herds! the cho - rus come and swell! Sing No - ël, O sing No - ël!

poco rit.

153

THE THREE KINGS

ABBIE FARWELL BROWN
From the French

Old French Song

Majestically

1 Yes - ter - day I met up - on the way The three great
2. Christ-mas day They went up - on their way, The three great

kings who came from for - eign re - gions. Yes - ter - day I met up - on the
kings with all the pre-cious treas-ure. Christ-mas day They went up - on their

way The three great kings in all their fine ar - ray, With chests of
way To seek a Ba - by ly - ing in the hay. The one a

gold and of gifts un - told. Then came the hosts of the march-ing, might-y
black king, and one was brown, Who came so far for a lit - tle Ba-by's

le - gions, With chests of gold and of gifts un -
pleas - ure; And one was white with a gold - en

told, The three great kings in all their fine ar - ray!
crown, The three great kings so gal - lant and so gay!

WE THREE KINGS OF ORIENT ARE

J. H. HOPKINS

Allegretto

1. We three kings of O - rient are; Bear - ing gifts we
2. Born a King on Beth - le - hem's plain, Gold I bring, to
3. Frank - in - cense to of - fer have I, In - cense owns a
4. Myrrh is mine; its bit - ter per - fume Breathes a life of
5. Glo - rious now be - hold him a - rise, King and God and

trav - erse a - far Field and foun - tain, moor and moun - tain,
crown him a - gain, King for - ev - er, ceas - ing nev - er,
De - i - ty nigh. Prayer and prais - ing, all men rais - ing,
gath - er - ing gloom, Sorrow - ing, sigh - ing, bleed - ing, dy - ing,
sac - ri - fice, Al - le - lu - ia; Al - le - lu - ia;

CHORUS *ff cresc. ad lib. a tempo*

Fol - low - ing yon - der star.
O - ver us all to reign.
Wor - ship him, God most High. O Star of won - der,
Sealed in the stone - cold tomb.
Earth to the heav'ns re - plies.

Star of night, Star with roy - al beau - ty bright, West - ward

lead - ing, still pro - ceed - ing, Guide us to thy per - fect light.

THE HOLLY AND THE IVY

English

THE TWELVE DAYS OF CHRISTMAS

Traditional Song

Allegretto

On the first day of Christ-mas my true love sent to me A part-ridge

in a pear tree. On the sec-ond day of Christ-mas my true love sent to me

Two tur-tle-doves and a part-ridge in a pear tree. tree.

*This phrase must be repeated in the following verses as many times as is required by the words as follow:—

On the third day—Three French hens, two turtle-doves, &c.
On the fourth day—Four calling birds, three French hens, &c.
On the fifth day—Five gold rings, four calling birds, &c.
On the sixth day—Six geese a-laying, five gold rings, &c.
On the seventh day—Seven swans a-swimming, six geese a-laying, &c.
On the eighth day—Eight maids a-milking, seven swans a-swimming, &c.
On the ninth day—Nine ladies dancing, eight maids a-milking, &c.
On the tenth day—Ten lords a-leaping, nine ladies dancing, &c.
On the eleventh day—Eleven pipers piping, ten lords a-leaping, &c.
On the twelfth day—Twelve drummers drumming, eleven pipers piping, &c.

RING OUT, WILD BELLS

TENNYSON

Marked

1. Ring out, wild bells, to the blue, blue sky, The fly-ing cloud, the frost-y light. The year is dy-ing in the night; Ring out, wild bells, Ring out, wild bells; Ring out, wild bells, and let him die.

2.
Ring out the old, ring in the new,
Ring, happy bells across the snow.
The year is going; let him go;
Ring out the false; ring out the false;
Ring out the false; ring in the true.

3.
Ring out the grief that saps the mind
For those that here we see no more;
Ring out the feud of rich and poor;
Ring in redress; ring in redress;
Ring in redress to all mankind.

4.
Ring out old shapes of foul disease;
Ring out the narrowing lust of gold;
Ring out the thousand wars of old;
Ring in the peace, ring in the peace;
Ring in the thousand years of peace.

5.
Ring in the valiant man and free,
The larger heart, the kindlier hand;
Ring out the darkness of the land,
Ring in the Christ; ring in the Christ;
Ring in the Christ that is to be.

VERDANT SPRING AND ROSY SUMMER

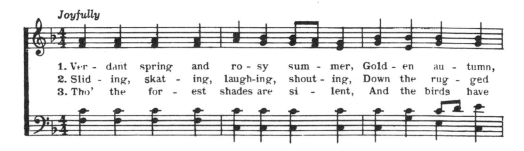

Joyfully

1. Ver-dant spring and ro-sy sum-mer, Gold-en au-tumn,
2. Slid-ing, skat-ing, laugh-ing, shout-ing, Down the rug-ged
3. Tho' the for-est shades are si-lent, And the birds have

JINGLE, BELLS

WE WISH YOU A MERRY CHRISTMAS

Joyously

1. We wish you a Mer-ry Christ-mas; We wish you a Mer-ry
2. We all want some fig-gy pud-ding; We all want some fig-gy
3. We all like fig-gy pud-ding, We all like fig-gy
4. We won't go un-til we get some; We won't go un-til we

Christ-mas, We wish you a Mer-ry Christ-mas, And a Hap-py New Year.
pud-ding; We all want some fig-gy pud-ding; So bring some out here.
pud-ding; We all like fig-gy pud-ding; So bring some out here.
get some; We wont go un-til we get some; So bring some out here.

CHORUS

Good tid-ing we bring To you and your kin. We

wish you a Mer-ry Christ-mas And a Hap-py New Year.

HERE WE COME A CAROLING

Old English

Traditional

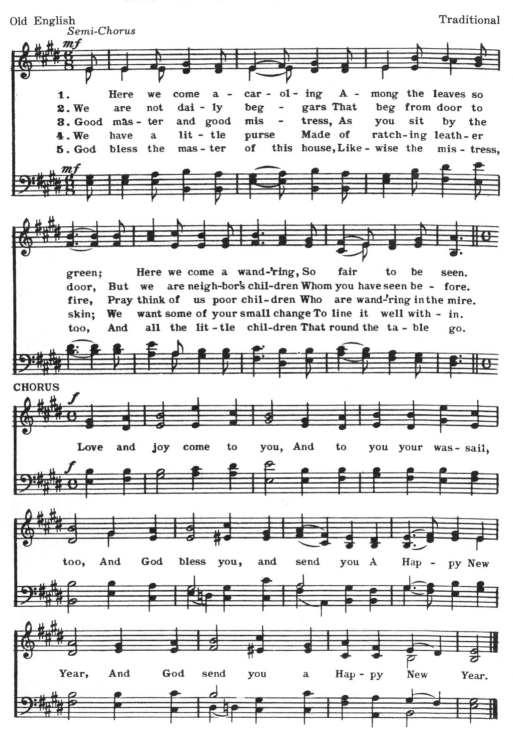

Semi-Chorus

1. Here we come a - car - ol - ing A - mong the leaves so
2. We are not dai - ly beg - gars That beg from door to
3. Good mas - ter and good mis - tress, As you sit by the
4. We have a lit - tle purse Made of ratch - ing leath - er
5. God bless the mas - ter of this house, Like - wise the mis - tress,

green; Here we come a wand-'ring, So fair to be seen.
door, But we are neigh-bor's chil-dren Whom you have seen be - fore.
fire, Pray think of us poor chil-dren Who are wand-'ring in the mire.
skin; We want some of your small change To line it well with - in.
too, And all the lit - tle chil-dren That round the ta - ble go.

CHORUS

Love and joy come to you, And to you your was - sail,

too, And God bless you, and send you A Hap - py New

Year, And God send you a Hap - py New Year.

AWAY IN A MANGER

MARTIN LUTHER

MARTIN LUTHER

Slowly

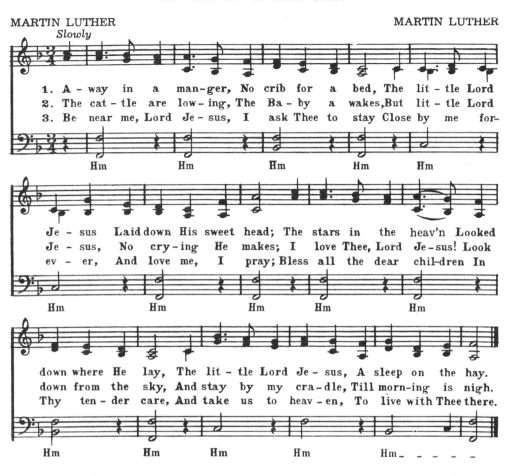

1. A - way in a man-ger, No crib for a bed, The lit - tle Lord
2. The cat - tle are low - ing, The Ba - by a wakes, But lit - tle Lord
3. Be near me, Lord Je - sus, I ask Thee to stay Close by me for-

Je - sus Laid down His sweet head; The stars in the heav'n Looked
Je - sus, No cry - ing He makes; I love Thee, Lord Je - sus! Look
ev - er, And love me, I pray; Bless all the dear chil-dren In

down where He lay, The lit - tle Lord Je - sus, A sleep on the hay.
down from the sky, And stay by my cra - dle, Till morn-ing is nigh.
Thy ten - der care, And take us to heav - en, To live with Thee there.

SLUMBER SONG

Translation

FRANZ SCHUBERT

Quietly

1. Slum-ber, slum-ber, ten-der lit-tle flow-er, Moth-er's lov-ing care
2. Slum-ber, slum-ber, lit-tle fad-ed flow-er, Still doth mother's love

doth a-round thee twine; Sweet and rest-ful be this hour;
a-round thee glow; Strong-er is it than earth-ly pow'r

Sooth-ing fall this lull-a-by of mine.
Guard-ing thee where e'er thy spir-it go.

HARK! HARK! THE LARK!

From Shakespeare's "Cymbeline"

FRANZ SCHUBERT

Hark! Hark! The Lark!

Hark! Hark! The Lark!

ev - 'ry thing that pret - ty bin, My la - dy sweet, a-

rise; A - rise, a - rise, my

la - dy sweet, a - rise; A - rise, a-

rise, my la - dy sweet, a - rise!

THE LINDEN TREE

Adapted from the German

FRANZ SCHUBERT

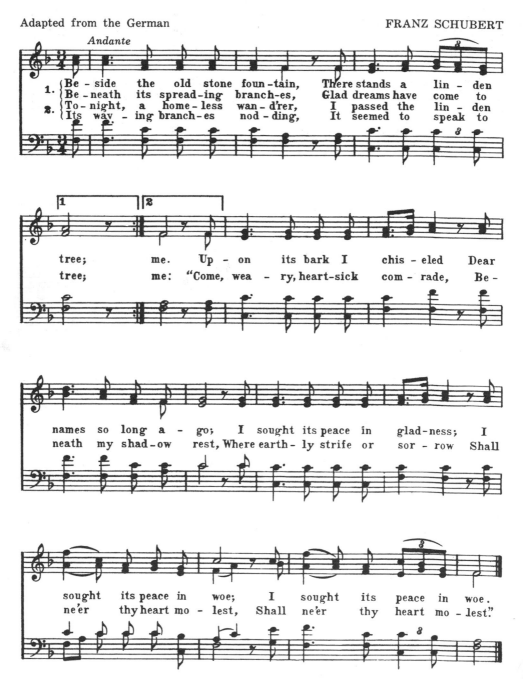

Andante

1. Be - side the old stone foun - tain, There stands a lin - den
   Be - neath its spread - ing branch - es, Glad dreams have come to

2. To - night, a home - less wan - d'rer, I passed the lin - den
   Its wav - ing branch - es nod - ding, It seemed to speak to

tree; me. Up - on its bark I chis - eled Dear
tree; me: "Come, wea - ry, heart-sick com - rade, Be -

names so long a - go; I sought its peace in glad - ness; I
neath my shad - ow rest, Where earth - ly strife or sor - row Shall

sought its peace in woe; I sought its peace in woe.
ne'er thy heart mo - lest, Shall ne'er thy heart mo - lest."

This song is complete in three parts and may be used as a trio for girls' voices, the alto tak-
ing the tenor with bass omitted.

CRADLE SONG

JOHANNES BRAHMS

1. Lul-la-by and good night! With ros-es be-
2. Lul-la-by and good night! Those blue eyes close

dight; Creep in-to thy bed; There pil-low thy
tight; Bright an-gels are near; So sleep with-out

head. If God will, thou shalt wake, When the morn-ing doth
fear. They will guard thee from harm, With fair dream-land's sweet

break; If God will, thou shalt wake, When the morn-ing doth break.
charm; They will guard thee from harm, With fair dream-land's sweet charm.

EURIDYCE, HERE I SEEK THEE

Aria-Orpheus

GLUCK

Tho' the earth be bright with flow - ers, And the smiles of dew-pearled mead-ows, Tho' glad-ness show'rs Thro' sun-lit hours, Life to me is dark with sor-rows, For my love lies in death's

Euridyce Here I Seek Thee

shad-ows. O the night of death is round me, And the deeps of grief en-

gulf me; Rise to greet me, Love in-vokes thee! Come to me be - lov - ed

one; Rise to greet me, Love in - vokes thee! Rise from death to love and

life, to love and life, to love and life.

THE LOST CHORD

ADELAIDE A. PROCTOR

Arr. by ARTHUR SULLIVAN

The Lost Chord

mu-sic like the sound of a great A - men, Like the sound of a

poco rall.

great A - men.

Girls Voices

It flood-ed the crim-son twi-light, Like the close of an An - gel's

Psalm, And it lay on my fev-ered spir - it,With a touch of in-fi-nite

The Lost Chord

The Lost Chord

The Lost Chord

GLORY NOW TO THEE BE GIVEN

From PHILIPP NICOLAI

J. S. BACH
In Seepers Wake!

1. Glo - ry now to thee be giv - en, On earth as in the high-
2. All of pearl each daz-zling por - tal, Where we shall join the song.

est heav - en. With lute and harp in sweet-est tone.
im - mor - tal, Of Saints and An-gels round Thy throne.

Be-yond all earth-ly ken Those joys di - vine re - main

That God pre - pares, Our hearts a - glow, Like

stars a - bove, Re - joice to feel His won - drous love.

GILBERT & SULLIVAN

THE FLOWERS THAT BLOOM IN THE SPRING

W. S. GILBERT

SIR ARTHUR SULLIVAN

The flow-ers that bloom in the spring,Tra la,Breathe promise of mer - ry sun-
The flow-ers that bloom in the spring,Tra la,Have noth-ing to do with the

shine. As we mer - ri - ly dance and we sing, Tra la, We
case. I've got to take un - der my wing, Tra la, A

wel-come the hope that they bring, Tra la, Of a sum-mer of ros - es so
most un-at-tract-ive old thing,Tra la,With a car - i - ca-ture of a

The Flowers That Bloom In The Spring

fine, Of a sum-mer of ros-es so fine; And that's what we
face, With a car - i - ca - ture of a face; And that's what I

mean when we say that a thing Is wel-come as flow-ers that
mean when I say or I sing, "Oh, both-er the flow-ers that

bloom in the spring; Tra, la, la, la, la, Tra, la, la, la, la, As we
bloom in the spring!" Tra, la, la, la, la, Tra, la, la, la, la, I've

mer - ri - ly dance and we sing, Tra, la, la, la, la, Tra,
got to take un - der my wing, Tra, la, la, la, la, Tra,

la, la, la, la, The flow-ers that bloom in the spring.
la, la, la, la, The flow-ers that bloom in the spring.

WE SAIL THE OCEAN BLUE

From "H.M.S. Pinafor"

W. S. GILBERT

SIR ARTHUR SULLIVAN

We sail the o-cean blue, And our sau-cy ship's a beau-ty; We're so-ber men and true, And at-ten-tive to our du-ty. When the balls whis-tle free O'er the bright blue sea, We stand to our guns all day. When at

We Sail The Ocean Blue

an–chor we ride On the Ports-mouth tide, We've plen-ty of time for play, A – hoy! A – hoy! The balls whis-tle free, A – hoy! A – hoy! O'er the bright blue sea, We stand to our guns, to our guns all day. We sail the o-cean blue, And our

We Sail The Ocean Blue

TARANTARA, TARANTARA

From "Pirates of Penzance"

W. S. GILBERT

SIR ARTHUR SULLIVAN

When the foe-man bares his steel, Ta-ran-ta-ra, Ta-ran-ta-ra, We un-com-for-ta-ble feel! Ta-ran-ta-ra, And we find the wis-est thing, Ta-ran-ta-ra, Ta-ran-ta-ra, Is to slap our chests and sing. Ta-ran-ta-ra!

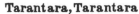

Tarantara, Tarantara

For when threatened with e-meutes, Ta-ran-ta - ra, Ta-ran-ta-ra,

And your heart is in your boots, Ta-ran-ta - ra, There is

noth - ing brings it 'round, Like the trum-pets mar - tial sound, Like the

trum - pets mar - tial sound! Ta-ran-ta - ra, ta-ran-ta -

184

Tarantara, Tarantara

185

TIT-WILLOW

W. S. GILBERT

From "The Mikado"

SIR ARTHUR SULLIVAN

Andante

1. On a tree by the riv-er a lit-tle tom-tit Sang "Wil-low, tit-wil-low, tit-wil-low!" And I said to him, "Dick-y bird, why do you sit Sing-ing wil-low, tit-wil-low, tit-wil-low? Is it weak-ness of in-tel-lect, bird-ie?" I cried, "Or a rath-er tough worm in your lit-tle in-side?" With a shake of his poor lit-tle

2. He slapped at his chest as he sat on the bough, Sing-ing "Wil-low, tit-wil-low, tit-wil-low!" And a cold per-spi-ra-tion be-span-gled his brow, "Oh, wil-low, tit-wil-low, tit-wil-low." He sobbed, and he sighed, and a gur-gle he gave. Then he threw him-self in-to the bil-low-y wave, And an ech-o a-rose from the

3. Now I feel just as sure as I'm sure that my name Isn't Wil-low, tit-wil-low, tit-wil-low! That 'twas blighted af-fec-tion that made him ex-claim, "Oh, wil-low, tit-wil-low, tit-wil-low." And if you re-main cal-lous and ob-du-rate, I shall per-ish as he did, and you will know why, Tho' I prob-ab-ly shall not ex-

Tit-Willow

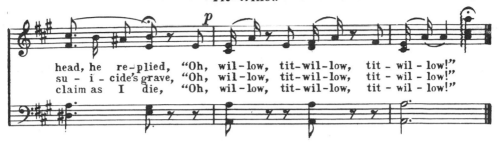

p

head, he re-plied, "Oh, wil-low, tit-wil-low, tit - wil - low!"
su - i - cide's grave, "Oh, wil-low, tit-wil-low, tit - wil - low!"
claim as I die, "Oh, wil-low, tit-wil-low, tit - wil - low!"

BUTTERCUP

W. S. GILBERT   From "H.M.S. Pinafore"   SIR ARTHUR SULLIVAN

Waltz Time

I'm called lit-tle But - ter- cup, Dear lit -tle But - ter- cup, Tho' I could
Then buy of your But - ter- cup, Dear lit -tle But - ter- cup, Sail-ors should

nev - er tell why. But still I'm called But - ter- cup, Poor lit - tle
nev - er be shy. So buy of your But - ter- cup, Poor lit - tle

But - ter - cup, Sweet lit-tle But - ter - cup, I.
But - ter - cup. Come, of your But - ter - cup buy.

MY OBJECT ALL SUBLIME

(The Mikado)

GILBERT and SULLIVAN

ONWARD, CHRISTIAN SOLDIERS

(6's & 5's D.)

S. BARING - GOULD

ARTHUR S. SULLIVAN

1. On-ward, Christian sol-diers, Marching as to war; With the cross of Je - sus Go - ing on be - fore. Christ, the roy-al Mas - ter, Leads a-gainst the foe; For-ward in - to bat - tle, See, His ban - ners go!

2. At the sign of tri-umph, Sa-tan's host doth flee; On, then, Christian sol diers, On to vic-to-ry. Hell's foun-da-tions quiv - er At the shout of praise; Broth-ers, lift your voic - es, Loud your an-thems raise.

3. Like a might-y ar - my Moves the Church of God; Brothers, we are tread - ing Where the saints have trod; We are not di - vid - ed, All one bod-y we, One in hope and doc - trine, One in char - i - ty.

4. On-ward, then, ye peo-ple, Join our hap-py throng, Blend with ours your voices In the tri-umph song; Glo-ry, laud, and hon - or, Un-to Christ the King. This thro' count-less a - ges Men and an-gels sing.

CHORUS

On-ward Christian sol - diers, Marching as to war, With the cross of Je-sus Go-ing on be-fore.

war, With the cross of Je-sus

189

HOME, SWEET HOME

JOHN HOWARD PAYNE   HENRY R. BISHOP

Reverently

1. Mid pleas-ures and pal - a - ces though we may roam, Be it
ev - er so hum - - ble, there's no place like home; A
charm from the skies seems to hal - low us there, Which,
seek thro' the world, is ne'er met with else-where.

2. I gaze on the moon as I tread the drear wild, And
feel that my moth - - er now thinks of her child, As she
looks on that moon from our own cot-tage door, Thro' the
wood - bine whose fragrance shall cheer me no more. Home, home,

3. An ex - ile from home splendor daz - zles in vain; Oh,
give me my low - - ly thatched cot - tage a - gain; The
birds sing - ing gai - ly, that came at my call, Give me
them, and that peace of mind dear - er than all.

Home, Sweet Home

sweet, sweet home, There's no place like home; There's no place like home.

IN THE TIME OF ROSES

Andante

J. REICHARDT

1. In the time of ro - ses, Hope, thou wear-y heart.
2. In the time of ro - ses, Wear-y heart, re - joice.

Spring a balm dis - clos - es For the keen - est smart.
E're the sum - mer clos - es Comes the long'd for voice.

Tho' thy grief o'er-come thee Thro' the win-ter's gloom,
Let not death ap - pal thee, For, be - yond the tomb,

Thou shalt thrust it from thee, When the ro - ses bloom.
God Him - self shall call thee, When the ro - ses bloom.

HOW CAN I LEAVE THEE

HELMINE VON CHEZY

Thuringian Folk Song

How can I leave thee! How can I from thee part! Thou on-ly
Blue is a flow'r-et called the "For-get-me-not," Wear it up-

hast my heart, Dear one, be-lieve. Thou hast this soul of mine,
on thy heart. And think of me! Flow'r-et and hope may die,

So close-ly bound to thine; No oth-er can I love, Save thee a-
Yet love with us shall stay; That can-not pass a-way, Dear one, be-

lone!
lieve.

dolce

IN THE GLOAMING

META ORRED

ANNIE F. HARRISON

Andante

In the gloam-ing oh, my dar-ling! when the lights are dim and low,
In the gloam-ing oh, my dar-ling! think not bit-ter-ly of me!

rall.

And the qui-et shad-ows, fall-ing, soft-ly come and soft-ly go;
Though I pass'd a-way in si-lence, left you lone-ly, set you free;

When the winds are sob-bing faint-ly with a gen-tle, un-known woe,
For my heart was crush'd with long-ing; what had been could nev-er be.

Will you think of me and love me, As you did once long a-go?
It was best to leave you thus, dear, Best for you and best for

rall. *cresc.*

me; It was best to leave you thus,— Best for you and best for me.—

MY OLD KENTUCKY HOME

STEPHEN C. FOSTER

Rather slow

1. The sun shines bright in the old Ken-tuck-y home; 'Tis
2. They hunt no more for the pos-sum and the coon On the
3. The head must bow, and the back will have to bend, Wher-

sum-mer, the dar-kies are gay; The corn-top's ripe and the
mead-ow, the hill and the shore; They sing no more by the
ev-er the dark-y may go; A few more days, and the

mead-ow's in the bloom While the birds make mu-sic all the day. The
glim-mer of the moon On the bench by the old cab-in door. The
trou-ble all will end In the field where the su-gar canes grow; A

young folks roll on the lit-tle ca-bin floor, All
day goes by like a sha-dow o'er the heart, With
few more days for to tote the wea-ry load, No

My Old Kentucky Home

mer - ry, all hap - py and bright; By'n - by hard times comes a -
sor - row where all was de - light; The time has come when the
mat - ter 'twill nev - er be light; A few more days till we

knock - ing at the door, Then my old Ken tuck-y home, good-night!
dark - ies have to part, Then my old Ken tuck-y home, good-night!
tot - ter on the road, Then my old Ken tuck-y home, good-night!

Weep no more, my la - dy; O weep no more to -

day! We will sing one song for the old Ken-tuck - y home, For the

old Ken - tuck - y home, far a - way.

GODFREY MARKS

Allegro

1. Y'heave ho! my lads, the wind blows free; A pleas - ant
2. The sail - or's life is bold and free; His home is

gale is on our lee, And soon a - cross the o - cean
on the roll - ing sea; And nev - er heart, more true or

clear, Our gal - lant bark shall brave - ly steer. But
brave Than his who launch - es on the wave; A -

Sailing

ere we part from Free-dom's shore to-night, A
far he speeds in dis-tant climes to roam; With

song we'll sing for home and beaut-y bright.
joy-ous song he rides the spark-ling foam.

Then here's to the sail-or, And here's to the heart so
Then here's to the sail-or, And here's to the heart so

true Who will think of him up-on the wa-ters blue.
true Who will think of him up-on the wa-ters blue.

Sailing

LISTEN TO THE MOCKING-BIRD

ALICE HAWTHORNE

Gently

1. I'm dream-ing now of Hal-ly, sweet Hal-ly, sweet Hal-ly; I'm
   She's sleep-ing in the val-ley, the val-ley, the val-ley; She's
2. Ah, well I yet re-mem-ber, re-mem-ber, re-mem-ber; Ah,
   'Twas in the mild Sep-tem-ber, Sep-tem-ber, Sep-tem-ber; 'Twas

dream-ing now of Hal-ly, For the thought of her is one that nev-er
sleep-ing in the val-ley, And the mock-ing-bird is sing-ing where she
well I yet re-mem-ber When we gath-ered in the cot-ton side by
in the mild Sep-tem-ber, And the mock-ing-bird was sing-ing far and

1. dies (omit)
2. lies.

side (omit) wide.

CHORUS

Lis-ten to the mock-ing-bird; Lis-ten to the mock-ing-bird, The mock-ing-bird still sing-ing o'er her grave. Lis-ten to the mock-ing-bird; Lis-ten to the mock-ing bird, Still sing-ing where the weep-ing wil-lows wave.

VIENNESE REFRAIN

Lyric by
HOWARD JOHNSON

Transcription by
HUGO FREY

An old re-frain is al-ways haunt-ing me, I heard in child-hood days
My cares and trou-bles used to steal a - way In my dear moth-er's arms

at moth-er's knee, There in the can-dle-light so ten-der - ly She'd sing a
at close of day; But now my wor-ries seem to ling-er long With-out the

song that lives in mem-o - ry, A strain of hap-pi - ness that dear - er
com-fort-ing of her sweet song. The fire-light gleamed up-on her sil - v'ry

Viennese Refrain

grows, A hymn of love that just a moth-er knows; And as my
hair, And o'er her head a ha-lo lin-gered there; And to this

tir-ed eyes be-gan to close, At peace with all the world I'd find re - pose.
an-gel sent from up a - bove I'd cling as she would sing her song of love.

Refrain

mf

Gone are those hap-py days so hea-ven sent. If I could live them o'er,

poco rit.

I'd be con-tent. Now ev-'ry night when shad-ows cov-er me, I miss that

poco rit.

201

Viennese Refrain

OH! SUSANNA

S.C.F.

STEPHEN C. FOSTER

CARRY ME BACK TO OLD VIRGINNY

J.B.

JAMES BLAND

1. Car-ry me back to old Vir-gin-ny. There's where the cot-ton and the corn and ta-ters grow; There's where the birds war-ble sweet in the spring-time; There's where the old dar-key's heart am long'd to go. There's where I la-bored so hard for old Mas-sa, Day af-ter

2. Car-ry me back to old Vir-gin-ny. There let me live till I with-er and de-cay. Long by the old Dis-mal Swamp have I wan-dered; There's where this old dar-key's life will pass a-way. Mas-sa and Mis-sis have long gone be-fore me; Soon we will

Carry Me Back To Old Virginny

day in the field of yel-low corn. No place on earth do I
meet on that bright and gold-en shore. There we'll be hap - py and

love more sin-cere-ly Than old Vir-gin-ny, the state where I was born.
free from all sor-row; There's where we'll meet and we'll nev-er part no more.

CHORUS

Car-ry me back to old Vir-gin-ny. There's where the cot-ton and the

corn and ta-ters grow; There's where the birds war-ble sweet in the

spring-time; There's where this old dar-key's heart am long'd to go.

OH, BOYS, CARRY ME 'LONG

STEPHEN C. FOSTER   STEPHEN C. FOSTER

Slowly

1. { Oh, car - ry me 'long; Der's no more trou - ble for
     worked long in de fields; I've han - dled man - y a
2. { Fare - well to de boys Wid hearts so hap - py an'
     Fare - well to de fields Ob cot - ton, 'bac - co an'

me; I's gwine to roam In a hap - py home Where
hoe; I'll turn my eye Be - fore I die, And
light; Dey sing a song de whole day long An'
all; I'se gwine to hoe in a bress - ed row Wha de

all de dar - keys am free. I've
see de su - gar - cane (*omit*) grow.
dance de ju - ba at night. An'
corn grows mel - low an' (*omit*) tall.

REFRAIN

Oh, boys, car - ry me' long; Car - ry me till I die.

Car - ry me down to de bu - ry - in' groun'. Mas - sa, don't you cry,

WHEN YOU AND I WERE YOUNG, MAGGIE

GEORGE W. JOHNSON

J. A. BUTTERFIELD

1. I wan-der'd to-day to the hill, Mag-gie, To watch the scene be - low, The creek and the old rust-y mill, Mag-gie, Where we sat in the long, long a - go. The green grove is gone from the hill, Mag-gie, Where first the dai - sies sprung; The old rust-y mill is still, Mag-gie, Since you and I were young.

2. A cit - y so si - lent and lone, Mag-gie, Where the young and the gay and the best, In pol - ish'd white man-sion of stone, Mag-gie, Have each found a place of rest, Is built where the birds used to play, Mag-gie, And join in the songs that were sung; For we sang just as gay as they, Mag-gie, When you and I were young.

3. They say I am fee - ble with age, Mag-gie; My steps are less spright-ly than then; My face is a well-writ-ten page, Mag-gie, But time a - lone was the pen. They say we are a - ged and gray, Mag-gie, As spray by the white breakers flung, But to me you're as fair as you were Mag-gie, When you and I were young.

MY BONNIE

Playfully

1. My Bon-nie lies o-ver the o-cean; My Bon-nie is o-ver the sea; My
2. O blow, ye winds, o-ver the o-cean, And blow ye winds o-ver the sea; O
3. Last night as I lay on my pil-low. Last night as I lay on my bed, Last

Bon-nie is o-ver the o-cean; O bring back my Bon-nie to me.
blow, ye winds, o-ver the o-cean, And bring back my Bon-nie to me.
night as I lay on my pil-low, I dreamed that my Bon-nie was dead.

Chorus

Bring back, bring back, Bring back my Bon-nie to me, to me;

Bring back, bring back, O bring back my Bon-nie to me.

THE CHURCH IN THE WILDWOOD

W.S.P.

DR. WM. S. PITTS

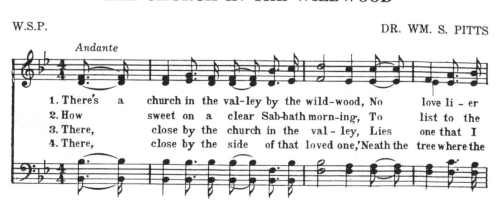

Andante

1. There's a church in the val-ley by the wild-wood, No love li - er
2. How sweet on a clear Sab-bath morn-ing, To list to the
3. There, close by the church in the val - ley, Lies one that I
4. There, close by the side of that loved one, 'Neath the tree where the

The Church In The Wildwood

place in the dale; No spot is so dear to my child - hood
clear ring - ing bell; Its tones so sweet - ly are call - ing:
loved so well; She sleeps, sweet-ly sleeps 'neath the wil - lows;
wild flow-ers bloom, When the fare - well hymn shall be chant - ed,

As the lit - tle brown church in the vale.
"Oh, come to the church in the vale."
Dis - turb not her rest in the vale.
I shall rest by her side in the tomb.

Chorus

Come to the church in the

Oh come, come, come, come, come, come, come, come,

wild - wood; oh, come to the church in the dale.

come, come, come, come, come, come, come, come, come, come, come, No

spot is so dear to my child-hood As the lit- tle brown church in the vale.

DIXIE LAND

D.D.E.

DANIEL D. EMMETT

Allegretto

I wish I was in the land ob cot - ton; Old times dar am
Old Mis-sus mar - ry Will, de wea - ber; Wil - lium was a
His face was sharp as a butch-er's clea - ber, But that did not

not for got - ten. Look a - way! Look a - way! Look a - way! Dix-ie
gay de-ceab-er. Look a - way! Look a - way! Look a - way! Dix-ie
seem to greab her. Look a - way! Look a - way! Look a - way! Dix-ie

Land. In Dix-ie Land whar' I was born in, Ear-ly on one
Land. But when he put his arm a-round 'er, He smil'd as fierce as a
Land. Old Mis-sus act-ed the fool-ish part, And died for a man dat

frost-y morn-in', Look a - way! Look a - way! Look a - way Dix-ie Land.
for - ty poun-der. Look a - way! Look a - way! Look a - way Dix-ie Land.
broke her heart. Look a - way! Look a - way! Look a - way Dix-ie Land.

CHORUS

Den I wish I was in Dix-ie, Hoo - ray! Hoo - ray! In Dix-ie Land, I'll

210

take my stand To lib an' die in Dix - ie; A - way, A - way, A -

way down south in Dix - ie; A - way, A - way, A - way down south in Dix - ie.

LONG, LONG AGO

THOS. HAYNES BAYLEY

Moderately

mf

1. Tell me the tales that to me were so dear, Long, Long, A-go, Long, Long A-go;
2. Do you re-men-ber the path where we met, Long, Long, A-go, Long, Long A-go;
3. Tho' by your kind-ness my fond hopes were rais'd, Long, Long, A-go, Long, Long A-go;

Sing me the songs I de - light-ed to hear, Long Long A-go, Long A - go.
Ah, yes, you told me you ne'er would for-get, Long Long A-go, Long A - go.
You, by more el - o-quent lips have been prais'd, Long Long A-go, Long A - go.

Now you are come, all my grief is re-mov'd, Let me for-get that so long you have rov'd
Then, to all oth-ers my smile you pre-ferr'd, Love, when you spoke, gave a charm to each word,
But by long ab-sence your truth has been tried, Still to your ac-cents I lis-ten with pride,

rall.

Let me be-lieve that you love as you lov'd, Long, Long A-go, Long A - go.
Still my heart treas-ures the prais-es I heard, Long, Long A-go, Long A - go.
Blest as I was when I sat by your side, Long, Long A-go, Long A - go.

KINGDOM COMING

MARBA C. JOSEPHSON

HENRY C. WORK
Arr. by MARGARET C. RICHARDS

1. Oh, sin-ners, men' yo ways an' pon-der' 'Bout de king-dom on its
2. De fi-ery fur-nace burns fo' you and me When we don't lib de

way. Go read yo Bi-ble; learn its les-sons; An' lib bet-ter eb-'ry
laws; But God will care fo' eb-'ry one of us Who tries to teach his

day. De Bi-ble say, lub eb-'ry man An don't take what is
cause. De He-brew chil-lun neb-er burned at all: Dey jes' walked 'round in

ders, To wor-ship right an' lub yo en-e-my. Be sure to say yo
glee, Cause God he hears de good man's prayer. Him he'll free from mis-er-

Kingdom Coming

Chorus

prayers.
y.

De Bi - ble say, lib right; And what it say, is so. It mus' be now de king-dom com-in'An' de year ob Ju-bi - lo.

THREE BLIND MICE

Three blind mice, Three blind mice, See how they run;

See how they run! They all ran af - ter the far-mer's wife; She

cut off their tails with a carv-ing knife; Did ev - er you see such a

sight in your life As three blind mice?

BEAUTIFUL DREAMER

STEPHEN C. FOSTER

1. Beau-ti-ful Dream-er, wake un-to me; Star-light and dew-drop are
2. Beau-ti-ful Dream-er, out on the sea, Mer-maids are chant-ing the

wait-ing for thee. Sounds of the rude world heard in the day,
wild lo-re-lei. O - ver the stream-let va-pors are borne,

Lull'd by the moon-light have all pass'd a - way! Beau-ti-ful Dream-er,
Wait-ing to fade at the bright com-ing morn. Beau-ti-ful Dream-er,

Beau - ti - ful

queen of my song, List while I woo Thee, with soft mel-o-dy;
beam on my heart, E'en as the moon on the stream-let and sea;

Gone are the cares of life's bu-sy throng; Beau-ti-ful Dream-er, a -
Then will all clouds of sor-row de-part;

wake un-to me! Beau-ti-ful Dream-er, a-wake un-to me.

SWEET AND LOW

ALFRED TENNYSON

J. BARNBY

1. Sweet and low, sweet and low, Wind of the west - ern sea;
2. Sleep and rest, sleep and rest; Fa-ther will come to thee soon;

Low, low, breathe and blow, Wind of the west - ern sea;
Rest, rest, on moth-er's breast, Fa-ther will come to thee soon;

1. O - ver the roll - ing wa - ters go; Come from the
   O - ver the wa - ters go; Come
2. Fa-ther will come to his babe in the nest, Sil - ver
   Fa - ther will come to his babe, Sil - ver

dy - ing moon and blow; Blow him a - gain to me,
from the moon and blow,
sails all out of the west, Un - der the sil - ver moon,
sails out the west,

While my lit - tle one, while my pret - ty one sleeps.
Sleep, my lit - tle one, sleep, my pret - ty one, sleep.

GRANDFATHER'S CLOCK

HENRY C. WORK

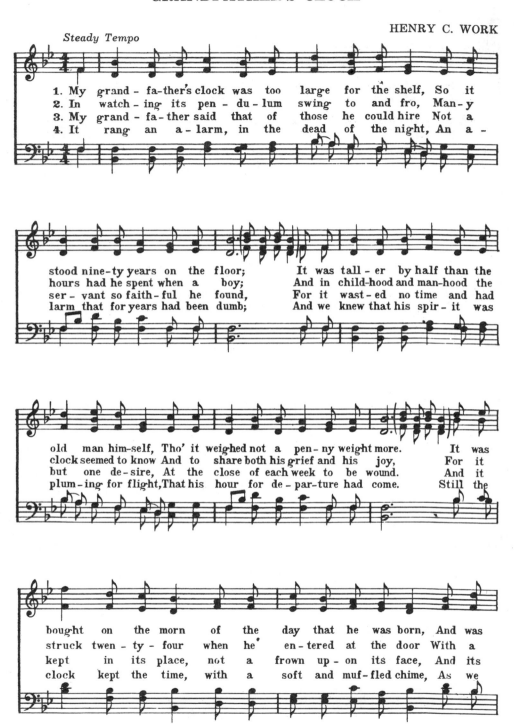

Grandfather's Clock

al - ways his trea - sure and pride; But it stopped, short,
bloom - ing and beau - ti - ful bride; But it stopped, short,
hands nev - er hung by its side; But it stopped, short,
si - lent - ly stood by his side; But it stopped, short,

nev - er to go a - gain When the old man died.
nev - er to go a - gain When the old man died.
nev - er to go a - gain When the old man died.
nev - er to go a - gain When the old man died.

Chorus

Nine - ty years with-out slum-ber-ing, tick, tock, tick, tock, His life seconds

num - ber - ing, tick, tock, tick, tock; It stopped, short,

nev - er to go a - gain, When the old man died.

217

LITTLE ANNIE ROONEY

MICHAEL NOLAN

1. A win-ning way, a pleas-ant smile, Dress'd so neat but quite in style, Mer-ry chaff your time to while, Has lit-tle An-nie Roon-ey. Ev'-ry ev-'ning rain or shine, I make a call 'twixt eight and nine, On her who short-ly will be mine, Lit-tle An-nie Roon-ey.

2. When mar-ried we'll so hap-py be, I love her, and she loves me; Hap-pier wife you'll nev-er see, Than lit-tle An-nie Roon-ey. In a lit-tle co-zy home, No more from her I'll care to roam; She'll greet you all when-e'er you come, Lit-tle An-nie Roon-ey.

REFRAIN

She's my sweet-heart; I'm her beau. She's my An-nie;

Little Annie Rooney

I'm her Joe. Soon we'll mar-ry, Nev-er to part.
Nev - er

Lit - tle An - nie Roon - ey   is   my   sweet - heart!

REUBEN AND RACHEL

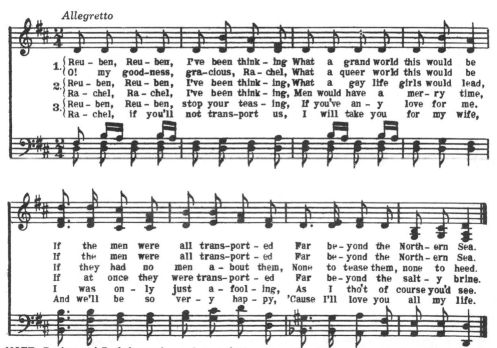

Allegretto

1. Reu - ben, Reu - ben, I've been think - ing What a grand world this would be
   O! my good-ness, gra-cious, Ra-chel, What a queer world this would be
2. Reu - ben, Reu - ben, I've been think - ing, What a gay life girls would lead,
   Ra - chel, Ra - chel, I've been think - ing, Men would have a mer - ry time,
3. Reu - ben, Reu - ben, stop your teas - ing, If you've an - y love for me.
   Ra - chel, if you'll not trans-port us, I will take you for my wife,

If the men were all trans-port - ed Far be - yond the North - ern Sea.
If the men were all trans-port - ed Far be - yond the North - ern Sea.
If they had no men a - bout them, None to tease them, none to heed.
If at once they were trans-port - ed Far be - yond the salt - y brine.
I was on - ly just a - fool - ing, As I tho't of course you'd see.
And we'll be so ver - y hap - py, 'Cause I'll love you all my life.

NOTE: Reuben and Rachel may be used as a duet number, the girls or women alternating with the boys or men through the several verses. The number may also be used effectively as a canon, in which case the first verse only would be used, the second part entering after the first part has sung two measures.

ANVIL CHORUS

(From "Il Trovatore")

GIUSEPPE VERDI

God of the na-tions, in glo-ry en thron-ed, Up-on our loved coun-try thy bless-ings pour; Guide us in wis-dom; let Truth live tri-umph-ant, And Free-dom a-bide with us ev-er - more!

Anvil Chorus

Proud-ly our ban - ner now gleam with gold-en lus - ter! Bright - er each star shines in the glo-rious clus-ter! Hail! Hail! Free - dom ev - er - more! And Truth tri- umph - ant, And Truth tri-umph - ant through-out our glo-rious land.

THANKSGIVING SONG

J.L.G.

JESSIE L. GAYNOR

Swinging

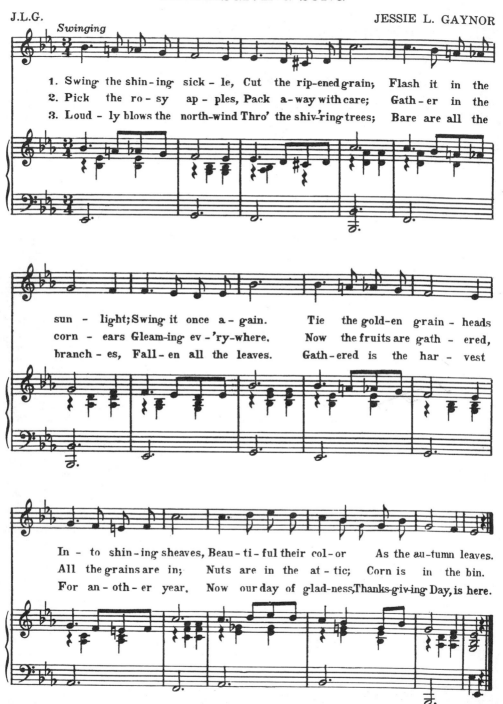

1. Swing the shin-ing sick-le, Cut the rip-ened grain; Flash it in the
2. Pick the ro-sy ap-ples, Pack a-way with care; Gath-er in the
3. Loud-ly blows the north-wind Thro' the shiv'-ring trees; Bare are all the

sun-light; Swing it once a-gain. Tie the gold-en grain-heads
corn-ears Gleam-ing ev-'ry-where. Now the fruits are gath-ered,
branch-es, Fall-en all the leaves. Gath-ered is the har-vest

In-to shin-ing sheaves, Beau-ti-ful their col-or As the au-tumn leaves.
All the grains are in; Nuts are in the at-tic; Corn is in the bin.
For an-oth-er year. Now our day of glad-ness, Thanks-giv-ing Day, is here.

SWEET GENEVIEVE

GEORGE COOPER

HENRY TUCKER

Andante

1. Oh, Gen - e - vieve, I'd give the world To live a - gain the love - ly past; The
2. Fair Gen - e - vieve, my ear - ly love, The years but make you dear - er far; My

rose of youth was dew im-pearl'd, But now it with-ers in the blast; I
heart shall nev - er, nev - er rove; Thou art my on - ly guid-ing star; For

see thy face in ev - 'ry dream; My wak - ing tho'ts are full of thee; Thy
me the past has no re - gret, What-e'er the years may bring to me; I

glance is in the star - ry beam That falls a - long the sum-mer sea.
bless the hour when first we met, The hour that gave me love and thee. Oh,

CHORUS

Gen - e - vieve, sweet Gen - e - vieve, The days may come, the days may go, But

still the hand of mem - 'ry weaves The bliss - ful dreams of long a - go.

AMERICA, THE BEAUTIFUL

KATHERINE LEE BATES

SAMUEL A. WARD

America, The Beautiful

mer - i - ca! All hail! All

shed his grace on thee, And crown thy good with
mend thine ev - 'ry flaw; Con - firm thy soil in
God thy gold re - fine Till all suc - cess be
shed his grace on thee, And crown thy good with

hail! Thy lib - er - ty in law.
From sea to shin - ing sea!

broth - er - hood, From sea to shin - ing sea.
self - con - trol, Thy lib - er - ty in law.
no - ble - ness, And ev - 'ry gain di - vine.
broth - er - hood, From sea to shin - ing sea.

ARE YOU SLEEPING?

Are you sleep-ing, are you sleep-ing, Bro-ther John, Bro-ther John.

Morn-ing bells are ring-ing; Morn-ing bells are ring-ing Ding, ding, dong, Ding, ding, dong.

The following words may be used to the above round. "Are You Sleeping?"

CHEER UP

Cheer up, ... , Cheer up, ... ,
Smile awhile, smile awhile;
'Tisn't going to hurt you,
'Tisn't going to hurt you,
Ha, ha, ha; ha, ha, ha.

BLACK-EYED SUSAN!

Black-eyed Susan! Black-eyed Susan!
How are you? How are you?
Very well, I thank you;
Very well, I thank you;
How are you? How are you?

RHEUMATISM

Rheumatism, rheumatism;
How it pains, how it pains!
Up and down the system,
Up and down the system,
When it rains, when it rains.

PERFECT POSTURE

Perfect posture! Perfect posture!
Do not slump, do not slump;
You must grow up handsome,
You must grow up handsome,
Hide that hump! Hide that hump!

225

OLD FOLKS AT HOME

S.C.F.

STEPHEN C. FOSTER

Old Folks At Home

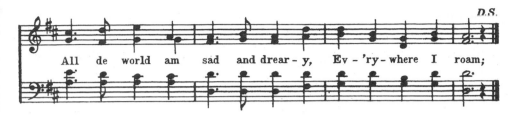

All de world am sad and drear-y, Ev-'ry-where I roam;

ALOHA OE

Andante

(LADIES VOICES) Fare-well to thee, Fare-well to thee,

(MEN'S VOICES) Fare - well to thee, Fare - well to thee, Thou

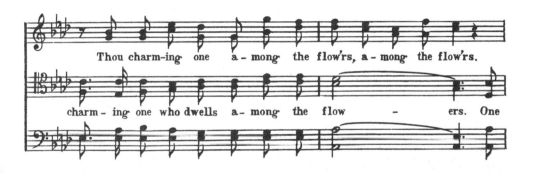

Thou charm-ing one a - mong the flow'rs, a - mong the flow'rs.

charm - ing one who dwells a - mong the flow - ers. One

one fond em-brace be-fore we part un-til we meet a-gain.

fond em - brace be - fore we part un - til we meet a - gain.

OLD BLACK JOE

Ladies Tri

STEPHEN FOSTER

Slowly

1. The days was young and
2. I weep should feel no
3. The hearts so glad and

CHORUS

1. Gone are the days when my heart was young and gay;
2. Why do I weep when my heart should feel no pain?
3. Where are the hearts once so hap-py and so free,

gay; my friends the fields a -
pain? I sigh come not a -
free? so dear up - on my

Gone are my friends from the cot - ton fields a - way;
Why do I sigh that my friends come not a - gain?
Chil - dren so dear that I held up - on my knee?

way; the earth to a bet - ter land I know,
grain? for forms now de - part - ed long a - go,
knee? the shores where my soul has long'd to go,

Gone from the earth to a bet - ter land I know,
Griev - ing for forms now de - part - ed long a - go,
Gone to the shores where my soul has long'd to go,

Old Black Joe

JOHN PEEL

With great spirit. Moderately fast

Old Air

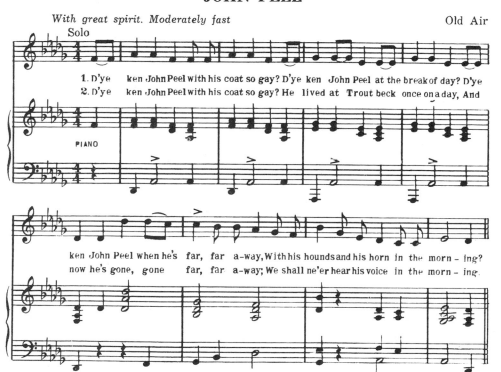

1. D'ye ken John Peel with his coat so gay? D'ye ken John Peel at the break of day? D'ye
2. D'ye ken John Peel with his coat so gay? He lived at Troutbeck once on a day, And

ken John Peel when he's far, far a-way, With his hounds and his horn in the morn - ing?
now he's gone, gone far, far a-way; We shall ne'er hear his voice in the morn - ing.

John Peel

RIO GRANDE

Sailors' Chantey

Love's Old Sweet Song

C. CLIFTON BINGHAM

MOLLOY

1. Once in the dear, dead days be-yond re-call, When on the world the
2. E - ven to-day we hear love's song of yore; Deep in our hearts it

mists be - gan to fall, Out of the dreams that rose in hap - py throng,
dwells for - ev - er-more; Foot-steps may fal - ter; wear - y grow the way;

Low to our hearts love sang an old, sweet song; And in the dusk, where
Still we can hear it at the close of day; So till the end, when

fell the fire-light gleam, Soft - ly it wove it-self in - to our dream.
life's dim shad-ows fall, Love will be found the sweetest song of all.

Love's Old Sweet Song

233

SWING LOW, SWEET CHARIOT

NONSENSE

VIVE L'AMOUR

Old Student Song

Allegro ♩. = 104

Solo ... Chorus

1. Let ev-'ry good fel-low now join in a song, Vi - ve la com-pa-gnie!
2. A friend on the left and a friend on the right, Vi - ve la com-pa-gnie!

Solo ... Chorus

Suc - cess to each oth-er and pass it a long, Vi - ve la com-pa-gnie!
In love and good fel-low-ship let us u-nite, Vi - ve la com-pa-gnie!

CHORUS

Vi - ve la, Vi - ve la, Vi - ve l'a-mour; Vi - ve la, Vi - ve la,

Vi - ve l'a-mour, Vi - ve l'a-mour; Vi - ve l'a-mour; Vi - ve la com pa - gnie!

AEREY, AEREY, IEREY-O

1. Eigh-teen hun-dred and for-ty one, That's the year my
2. Eigh-teen hun-dred and for-ty-two, Did-n't know just
3. Eigh-teen hun-dred and for-ty-three, That's the year I

trou-bles be-gan; That's the year my troubles began; A-work-in on the rail-road.
what to do; Did-n't know just what to do; So I worked on the rail-road.
crossed the sea; That's the year I crossed the sea, To work up-on the rail-road.

Ae - rey, Ae - rey, Ie - rey - O, Ae - rey, Ae - rey, Ie - rey - O,

Ae - rey, Ae - rey, Ie - rey - O, A work - in' on the rail - road.

Aerey, Aerey, Ierey-O

4. Eighteen hundred and forty-four
   Bless the ship that brought me o'er,
   Bless the ship that brought me o'er
   To work upon the railroad.

5. Eighteen hundred and forty-five
   I'd rather be dead than be alive,
   I'd rather be dead than be alive
   To work upon the railroad.

6. Eighteen hundred and forty-six,
   Shouldered my shovel and picked up my picks,
   Shouldered my shovel and picked up my picks
   To work upon the railroad.

7. Eighteen hundred and forty-seven,
   That's the year I went to heaven,
   That's the year I went to heaven
   To work upon the railroad.

8. Eighteen hundred and forty-eight,
   St. Peter said I was too late,
   St. Peter said I was too late
   To work upon the railroad.

9. Eighteen hundred and forty-nine,
   The devil said I was in time,
   The devil said I was in time
   To work upon the railroad.

10. Eighteen hundred and fifty,
    From then until eternity,
    From then until eternity
    I worked upon his railroad.

FOR HE'S A JOLLY GOOD FELLOW

OUR BOYS WILL SHINE TO-NIGHT

Our Boys Will Shine To-Night

shine. When the sun goes down and the moon comes up, Our boys will shine.

STYLE ALL THE WHILE

Fast

They say that *Supply name* he/they she ain't got no style. Got style all the while,

got style all the while. They say that *Supply name* he/they she ain't got no style. Got style all the while, all the while.____ yip yip

239

A MERRY LIFE

Funiculi, Funicula

From The Italian

LUIGI DENZA

A Merry Life

241

A Merry Life

First time Solo, second time Chorus

Hark - en! Hark - en! Mu - sic sounds a - far! Hark - en! Hark - en!

Hark - en! Hark - en! Mu - sic sounds a - far! Hark - en! Hark - en!

Mu - sic sounds a - far, Tra-la-la - la - la, tra-la - la - la, tra-la-la - la, tra-la-la-la!

Mu - sic sounds a - far, Tra-la-la - la, tra-la - la - la, tra-la-la - la, tra-la-la-la!

Joy is ev - 'ry - where, Tra-la - la-la, tra-la - la-la.

Joy is ev - 'ry - where, Tra-la - la-la, tra-la - la-la.

BILLY BOY

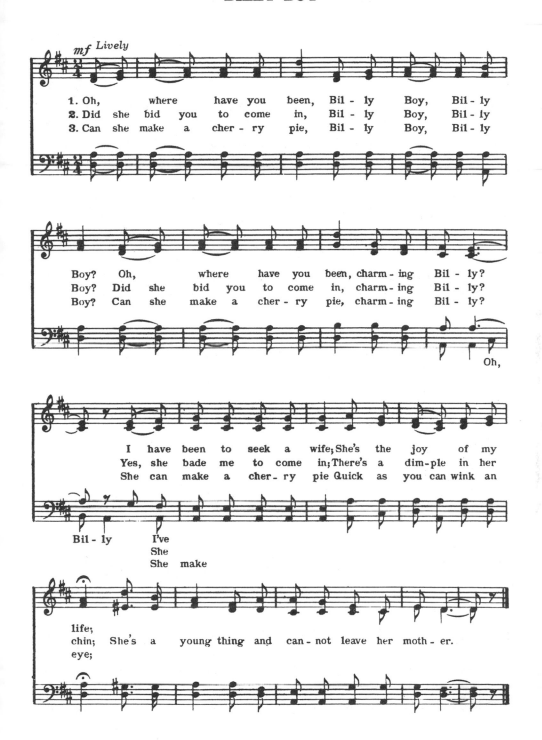

1. Oh, where have you been, Bil - ly Boy, Bil - ly
2. Did she bid you to come in, Bil - ly Boy, Bil - ly
3. Can she make a cher - ry pie, Bil - ly Boy, Bil - ly

Boy? Oh, where have you been, charm - ing Bil - ly?
Boy? Did she bid you to come in, charm - ing Bil - ly?
Boy? Can she make a cher - ry pie, charm - ing Bil - ly?

Oh,

I have been to seek a wife; She's the joy of my
Yes, she bade me to come in; There's a dim - ple in her
She can make a cher - ry pie Quick as you can wink an

Bil - ly I've
She
She make

life;
chin; She's a young thing and can - not leave her moth - er.
eye;

SOUTHERN MEMORIES

Southern Memories

hal - le - lu, hal - le - lu - ia! lu - ia! Hear them bells, don't you hear them bells?

They are ring - ing out the glo - ry hal - le - lu!

NIGHT SONG

Moderato

Now run a-long home and jump in-to bed and say your prayers and cover your head. If

you'll promise me, Then I'll promise you; If you'll pray for me, Then I'll pray for you.

SOLOMON LEVI

College Song

THE SPANISH CAVALIER

W.D.H.

W. D. HENDRICKSON

1. A Span-ish Cav-a-lier stood in his re-treat, And
2. I'm off to the war; to the war I must go, To
3. And when the war is o'er, to you I'll re-turn, A-

on his gui-tar played a tune, dear; The mu-sic so sweet Would
fight for my coun-try and you, dear; But if I should fall, In
gain to my coun-try and you, dear; But if I be slain, You may

oft-times re-peat The bless-ing of my coun-try and you, dear.
vain I would call, The bless-ing of my coun-try and you, dear.
seek me in vain, Up-on the bat-tle-field you will find me.

CHORUS

Oh, say, dar-ling, say, when I'm far a-way, Sometimes you may think of me, dear;

Bright sun-ny days will soon fade a-way, Re-mem-ber what I say, and be true, dear.

RIG-A-JIG

Allegro

1. As I was walk-ing down the street, Heigh-o! heigh-o! heigh-
2. Said I to her,"What is your trade?"Heigh-o! heigh-o! heigh-

o! heigh-o! A pret-ty girl I chanced to meet, Heigho! heigho! heigh-o!
o! heigh-o! Said she to me,"I'm a weav-er's maid."Heigho! heigho! heigh-o!

Rig-a-jig-jig, and a-way we go, A-way we go, a-way we go,

Rig-a-jig-jig, and a-way we go, Heigh-o! heigh-o! heigh-o! Heigh-

o! heigh-o! heigh-o! heigh-o! heigh-o! heigh-o! heigh-o! heigh-o!

Rig-a-jig-jig, and a-way we go, Heigh-o! heigh-o! heigh-o!

the man on the flying trapeze

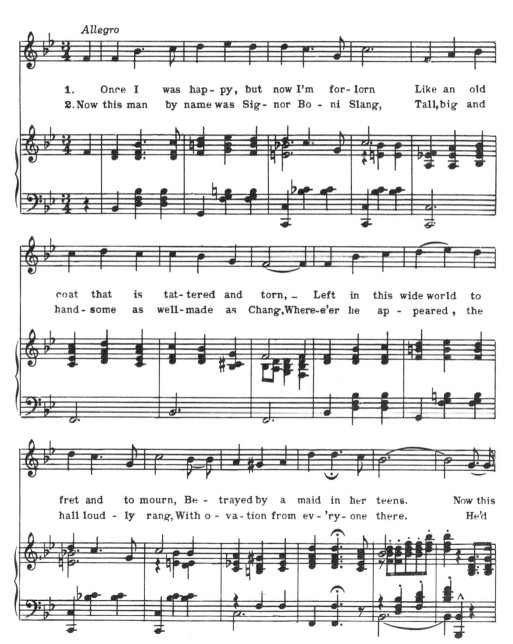

Allegro

1. Once I was hap-py, but now I'm for-lorn Like an old
2. Now this man by name was Sig- nor Bo - ni Slang, Tall, big and

coat that is tat-tered and torn, — Left in this wide world to
hand- some as well-made as Chang. Where-e'er he ap - peared , the

fret and to mourn, Be - trayed by a maid in her teens. Now this
hall loud - ly rang, With o - va - tion from ev-'ry- one there. He'd

The Man On The Flying Trapeze

girl that I loved she was hand-some, And I tried all I
smile from the bar on all peo-ple be-low, And one night he

knew her to please. But I nev-er could please her one
smiled on my love. She winked back at him, and she

quar-ter so well, As the man on the fly-ing trap-eze.
shout-ed "Bra-vo," As he hung by his nose up a-bove.

CHORUS

He flies through the air with the great-est of ease, This dar-ing young
Last only She floats through the air with the great-est of ease; You'd think her a

The Man On The Flying Trapeze

man   on   the   fly - ing   trap - eze.   His move-ments are   grace-ful; all
man   on   the   fly - ing   trap - eze.   She does   all   the   work while he

girls   he   does please,   And my   love he's   pur - loin - ed   a - way.
sure takes   his   ease,   And   that's what's be-come   of   my   love.

3. Her father and mother were both on my side
   And very hard tried to make her my own bride,
   Her father he sighed and her mother she cried,
   To see her throw herself away.

4. "Twas all no avail, she went there every night,
   And threw him bouquets on the stage,
   Which caused her to meet him; how he ran me down!
   To tell it would take a whole page.

5. One night I, as usual, went to her dear home,
   Found there her mother and father alone;
   I asked for my love, and soon 'twas made known,
   To my horror that she'd run away.

6. She packed up her boxes and eloped in the night,
   With him with the greatest of ease;
   From two stories high he had lowered her down,
   To the ground on his flying trapeze.

7. Some months after that I went into a hall;
   To my surprise I found there on a wall,
   A bill in red letters which did my heart gall,
   That she was appearing with him.

8. He'd taught her gymnastics, and dressed her in tights,
   To help him to live at his ease;
   He'd made her assume a masculine name,
   And now she goes on the trapeze.

ALOUETTE

French-Canadian Folk Song

A-lou-et-te, gen-tille A-lou-et-te, A-lou-et-te,

Je te plum me-rai.

1. Je te plu-me-rai la tête.
2. Je te plu-me-rai le bec.

Je te plu-me-rai la tête,
Je te plu-me-rai le bec,

1. Et la tête, et la tête.
2. { Et le bec, et le bec. Oh!
{ Et la tête, et la tête.

3. Le nez.   4. Le dos.   5. Les pattes.   6. Le cou.

See footnote★

★ After first verse, repeat this measure with the words in reverse order; for example, the last verse will be as follows:"Et le cou, et le pattes, et le dos, et le nez, et le bec, et la tète, Oh, Alouette, etc"

252

UPIDEE

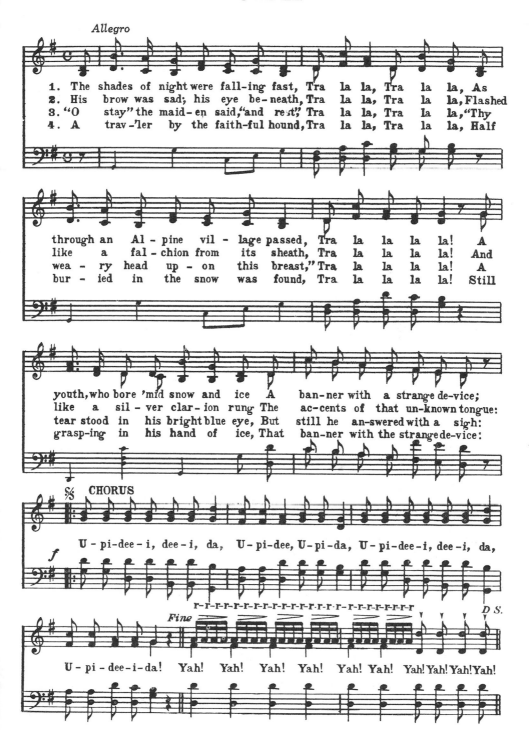

Allegro

1. The shades of night were fall-ing fast, Tra la la, Tra la la, As
2. His brow was sad; his eye be-neath, Tra la la, Tra la la, Flashed
3. "O stay" the maid-en said,"and rest," Tra la la, Tra la la, "Thy
4. A trav-'ler by the faith-ful hound,Tra la la, Tra la la, Half

through an Al - pine vil - lage passed, Tra la la la la! A
like a fal - chion from its sheath, Tra la la la la! And
wea - ry head up - on this breast,"Tra la la la la! A
bur - ied in the snow was found, Tra la la la la! Still

youth,who bore 'mid snow and ice A ban-ner with a strange de-vice;
like a sil - ver clar- ion rung The ac-cents of that un-known tongue;
tear stood in his bright blue eye, But still he an-swered with a sigh:
grasp-ing in his hand of ice, That ban-ner with the strange de-vice:

CHORUS

f U - pi-dee - i, dee - i, da, U - pi-dee, U-pi-da, U-pi-dee-i, dee-i, da,

Fine U - pi - dee-i-da! Yah! Yah! Yah! Yah! Yah! Yah! Yah! Yah! Yah! Yah!

D S.

DICKORY, DICKORY, DOCK

Lively Allegretto

Dick - o - ry, dick - o - ry, dock; tick, tock. The

mouse ran up the clock; tick, tock. The clock struck "one," The

mouse ran down; Dick- o - ry, dick - o - ry, dock; tick, tock.

OH! WE CAN PLAY

In march time

Old Song

Oh! we can play on the big bass drum, And this is the way we

(OTHER INSTRUMENTS)

CHORUS

D.C.

do it: Rub dub dub on the big bass drum, And this is the way we do it.

O NO, JOHN!

Old English

Moderato

1. On yon-der hill there stands a crea-ture; Who she is, I
2. My fa-ther was a Span-ish cap-tain, Went to sea a
3. O mad-am, in your face is beau-ty; On your lips red
4. O mad-am, I will give you jew-els; I will make you

do not know. I'll go and court her for her beau-ty.
month a - go; First he kissed me; then he left me;
ros - es grow; Will you take me for your lov - er?
rich and free; I will give you silk - en dress-es;

She must an-swer, Yes or No. O No, John! No, John! No, John! No!
Bade me al-ways an-swer No. O No, John! No, John! No, John! No!
Mad-am, an-swer, Yes or No. O No, John! No, John! No, John! No!
Mad-am, will you mar-ry me? O No, John! No, John! No, John! No!

5. Oh madam, since you are so cruel,
And that you do scorn me so,
If I may not be your husband,
Madam, will you let me go?

6. O hark! I hear the churchbells ringing,
Will you come and be my wife?
Or, dear madam, have you settled
To live single all your life?

OH, MY DARLING CLEMENTINE

Allegretto

P. MONTROSE

1. In a cav-ern, in a can-yon, Ex-ca-vat-ing for a mine, Dwelt a min-er, for-ty nin-er, And his daugh-ter Cle-men-tine.
2. Light she was and like a fai-ry, And her shoes were num-ber nine; Her-ring box-es, with-out top-ses, San-dals were for Cle-men-tine.
3. Drove she duck-lings to the wat-er, Ev'-ry morn-ing just at nine, Hit her foot a-gainst a splin-ter, Fell in-to the foam-ing brine.
4. Ru-by lips a-bove the wat-er, Blow-ing bub-bles soft and fine; A-las, for me! I was no swim-mer; So I lost my Cle-men-tine.

REFRAIN

Oh, my dar-ling, Oh, my dar-ling, Oh, my dar-ling Cle-men-tine, You are lost and gone for-ev-er, Oh, my dar-ling Cle-men-tine.

O ME! O MY!

(A TOAST)

(Substitute any name for the words "the speaker")

O me! O my! We'll get there by and by. If an-y-bo-dy likes the speak-er, It's I, I, I, I, I.
O my! O me! We're hap-py as can be. If an-y-bo-dy likes the speak-er, It's me, me, me, me, me

O me! O my! We'll get there by and by. If anybody likes the speaker It's I, I, I, I, I.
O my! O me! We're happy as can be. If anybody likes the speaker, It's me, me, me, me, me.

NOAH'S ARK

POLLY - WOLLY - DOODLE

Moderato

1. Oh, I went down South for to see my Sal; Sing Pol-ly-wol-ly-doo-dle all the
2. Oh, my Sal, she am a maid-en fair;

day. My Sal-ly am a spunk-y gal;
With cur-ly eyes and laughing hair, Sing Pol-ly-wol-ly-doo-dle all the

day. Fare thee well Fare thee well Fare thee
Fare-well Fare-well

well, my fair-y fay, For I'm goin' to Louis-i-an-na, For to

see my Su-sy-an-na, Sing Pol-ly-wol-ly-doo-dle all the day.

A grasshopper sitting on a railroad track,
Sing Polly-wolly-doodle all the day,
A picking his teeth with a carpet tack,
Sing Polly-wolly-doodle all the day.

THE KEYS OF HEAVEN

Old English

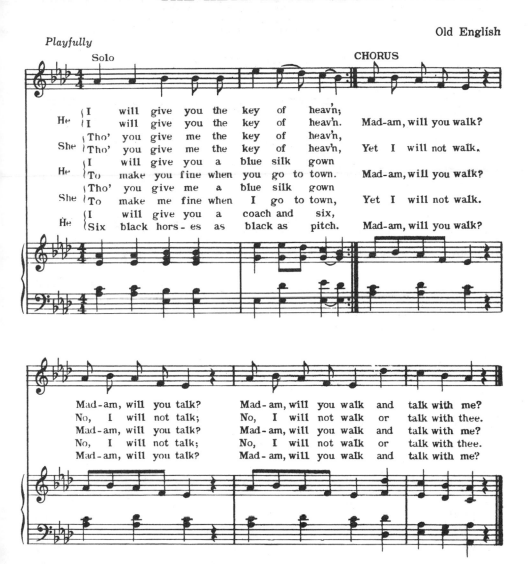

Playfully

He: {I will give you the key of heav'n;
I will give you the key of heav'n. Mad-am, will you walk?

She: {Tho' you give me the key of heav'n,
Tho' you give me the key of heav'n, Yet I will not walk.

He: {I will give you a blue silk gown
To make you fine when you go to town. Mad-am, will you walk?

She: {Tho' you give me a blue silk gown
To make me fine when I go to town, Yet I will not walk.

He: {I will give you a coach and six,
Six black hors-es as black as pitch. Mad-am, will you walk?

Mad-am, will you talk? Mad-am, will you walk and talk with me?
No, I will not talk; No, I will not walk or talk with thee.
Mad-am, will you talk? Mad-am, will you walk and talk with me?
No, I will not talk; No, I will not walk or talk with thee.
Mad-am, will you talk? Mad-am, will you walk and talk with me?

She: Tho' you give me a coach and six,
Six black horses as black as pitch, Yet I will not walk,
No, I will not talk. No, I will not walk or talk with thee.

He: I will give you the keys of my heart,
And we'll be married till death us do part. Madam, will you walk?
Madam, will you talk? Madam, will you walk and talk with me?

She: Thou shalt give me the keys of thy heart,
And we'll marry till death do us part, Yes, Now I will walk.
Yes, now I will walk. Yes, now I will walk and talk with thee.

This song is dramatized as follows: during each verse two girls bring to a boy (Soldier) the article mentioned in that verse, which the Soldier puts on. After the last verse (which ends with the words: "wife of my own,") the music is hummed while all the girls indignantly deprive the Soldier of the apparel he has fraudulently obtained.

O SOLDIER, SOLDIER

Old English, Traditional

(Girls) *Allegro*

"O sol-dier, sol-dier, won't you mar-ry me? With your mus-ket, fife and drum?"

(Boys) *Fine*

"Oh, no, sweet maid, I can-not mar-ry thee, for { I have no coat / I have no hat / I have no gloves } to put on."
I have a wife of my own." *End*

(All)

Then up she went to her grand-fa-ther's chest, And got him a

{ coat / hat / pair } of the ver-y, ver-y best; She got him a { coat / hat / pair }

D.C.

of the ver-y, ver-y best, And the sol-dier put { it / it / them } on.

260

SOME FOLKS

S.C.F.

STEPHEN C. FOSTER

1. Some folks like to sigh. Some folks do, some folks do;
2. Some folks fear to smile. Some folks do, some folks do;
3. Some folks fret and scold. Some folks do, some folks do;
4. Some folks get gray hairs. Some folks do, some folks do;
5. Some folks toil and save. Some folks do, some folks do;

Some folks long to die, But that's not me nor you.
Oth - ers laugh thro' guile. But that's not me nor you.
They'll soon be dead and cold, But that's not me nor you.
Brood - ing o'er their cares, But that's not me nor you.
To buy themselves a grave, But that's not me nor you.

CHORUS

Long live the mer-ry, mer-ry heart That laughs by night and day, Like the

Queen of mirth, No mat-ter what some folks say.

MISTRESS SHADY

Allegro

American College Song

Oh, Mis tress Sha - dy, She is a la - dy;

She has a daugh - ter whom I a - dore.

Each day I court her, I mean the daugh - ter,

Ev - r'y Sun - day, Mon - day, Tues - day, Wednesday, Thursday, Fri - day,

Satur - day, Sun - day af - ter-noon at half past four.

THE DEAF WOMAN'S COURTSHIP

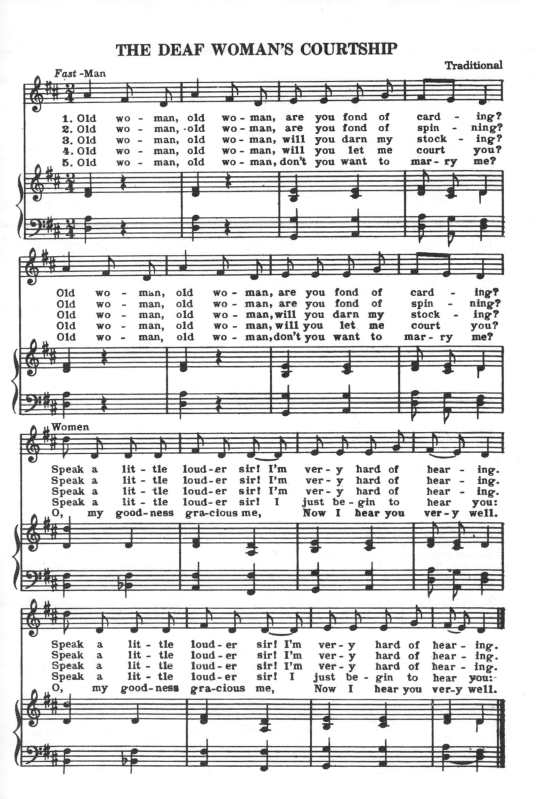

Traditional

Fast -Man

1. Old wo - man, old wo - man, are you fond of card - ing?
2. Old wo - man, old wo - man, are you fond of spin - ning?
3. Old wo - man, old wo - man, will you darn my stock - ing?
4. Old wo - man, old wo - man, will you let me court you?
5. Old wo - man, old wo - man, don't you want to mar - ry me?

Old wo - man, old wo - man, are you fond of card - ing?
Old wo - man, old wo - man, are you fond of spin - ning?
Old wo - man, old wo - man, will you darn my stock - ing?
Old wo - man, old wo - man, will you let me court you?
Old wo - man, old wo - man, don't you want to mar - ry me?

Women

Speak a lit - tle loud - er sir! I'm ver - y hard of hear - ing.
Speak a lit - tle loud - er sir! I'm ver - y hard of hear - ing.
Speak a lit - tle loud - er sir! I'm ver - y hard of hear - ing.
Speak a lit - tle loud - er sir! I just be - gin to hear you:
O, my good - ness gra - cious me, Now I hear you ver - y well.

Speak a lit - tle loud - er sir! I'm ver - y hard of hear - ing.
Speak a lit - tle loud - er sir! I'm ver - y hard of hear - ing.
Speak a lit - tle loud - er sir! I'm ver - y hard of hear - ing.
Speak a lit - tle loud - er sir! I just be - gin to hear you:
O, my good - ness gra - cious me, Now I hear you ver - y well.

LITTLE JACK HORNER

Brightly

Lit-tle Jack Hor-ner sat in a cor-ner eat-ing a Christ-mas pie. He

put in his thumb and pulled out a plumb, And said what a big boy am I.

Girls

What a big boy What a big boy What a big boy am I.

Boys

DOWN WHERE THE WATERMELONS GROW

Solo
Chorus

1. Ah's got a gal in Car-o-line Down where de wa-ter-mel-ons grow.
2. Ah went to see her one night in May Down where de wa-ter-mel-ons grow.

Solo
Chorus

Some sweet day she will be mine.
Ah's now gettin' ready for ma' wed-din' day. Down where de wa-ter-mel-ons grow.

Mem

Down where de wa-ter-mel-ons grow, How ah love her no-body knows Ah

Chorus

allus go to see'-er In mah Sunday meetin' clothes Down where the wa-ter-mel-ons grow.

264

CAMPTOWN RACES

STEPHEN C. FOSTER

1. De Camp-town la - dies sing dis song, Doo-dah! Doo-dah! De
2. De long tail'd filly and de big black hoss, Doo-dah! Doo dah! Dey

Camp-town race track nine miles long, Oh! Doo-dah day! I came down dar wid my
fly de track and de both cut a-cross, Oh! Doo-dah day! De blind hoss stick'n in a

hat cav'd in, Doo-dah! Doo-dah! I go back home with a pocket full of tin,
big mud hold, Doo-dah! Doo-dah! Can't touch bottom wid a ten foot pole,

Oh! Doo-dah day! Gwine to run all night; Gwine to run all day. I'll
Oh! Doo-dah day!

bet my mon-ey on de bob-tail nag, Some-bod-y bet on de bay.

EVALINA DEAR

Male Voices

Allegro

1. Way down in the mead-ow Where the lil - y first blows, Where the
2. She's fair as a rose; like a lamb she is meek, And she

wind from the moun-tain ne'er ruf - fles the rose, Lives
nev - er was known to put paint on her cheek. In the

dear Ev - a - li - na, the sweet lit - tle dove, The
most grace - ful curls hangs her rav - en black hair, And she

pride of the val - ley, the girl that I love.
nev - er re - quires per - fum - er - y there.

Dear Ev - a - li - na, Sweet Ev - a - li - na,

Evalina Dear

My love for you shall nev - er, nev - er die.

Dear Ev - a - li - na, Sweet Ev - a - li - na,

My love for you shall nev - er, nev - er die.

GOOD FELLOWS

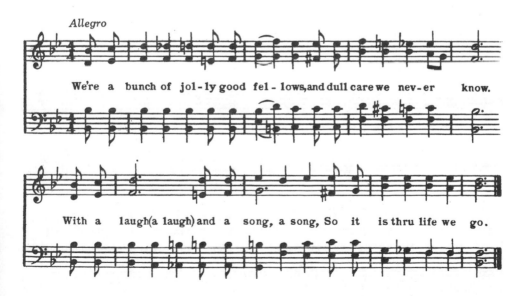

Allegro

We're a bunch of jol - ly good fel - lows, and dull care we nev - er know.

With a laugh (a laugh) and a song, a song, So it is thru life we go.

HARK, I HEAR A VOICE

Male Voices

DON'T GO AWAY AND LEAVE ME

Fast

Don't go a-way and leave me; Why don't you stay and spoon?

If you should go 'twould grieve me. Stay neath the sil-v'ry moon.

I like your styl-ish man-ner; I like your win-some smile.

I got a tale to tell you ('Bout what) 'Bout a cro-co-dile

SPOKEN

isle. O Ev-a-line, O Ev-a-line, say you'll be

mine (Say you'll be mine). Whis-per soft-ly, hon-ey, You'll be

Don't Go Away And Leave Me

mine (Ah, mine). 'Way down yon-der in de ole corn field For

you (For you) I pine (I pine); Sweet-er than the hon-ey

to the hon-ey bee, I love you; say you love me. Meet me in the

shade of the old ap-ple tree, Miss Ev-a - line, Ev-a - line.

Hand me down my bon-net; Hand me down my shawl; Hand me down my

cal-i-co dress, I'm go-ing to the cal-i-co ball. First she gave me

Don't Go Away And Leave Me

hon-ey; Then she gave me cake; Then she gave me gin-ger bread for kiss-ing her

at the gate, HUMMING   BUSINESS OF KISSING   At the gate.

HE MET HER ON THE STAIRS

Moderato

He met her on the stairs; 'Twas dark, and so he kissed her. He
He held her dain-ty hand, Quite glad he had not missed her. She

said, I beg your par - don. He said, I beg your par-don. I
mur-mured, Please don't men-tion it. She mur-mured, Please don't

thot it was my sis-ter.   men-tion it. Great Scott, great Scott, it was his sis-ter.

LEVEE SONG

Oh, I was born in Mo-bile town; I'm
All day I roll de cot-ton down a wuk-kin' on de le-vee.

I bin wuk-kin on de rail-road all de lib-long day.

I bin wuk-kin on de rail-road to pass de time a - way.

Doan yo' hear de whis-tle blow-in' Rise up so ear-ly in de mawn?

Doan ye hyar de cap-tain shout-in', Din-ah, blow yo' hawn?

Levee Song

Swinging

Sing a song of cit-ies. Give that bail a jerk.

Folks ain't half so hap-py as when they're hard at work:

Nor-folk for its oys-tah shells, Bos-ton for its beans,

Charle-ston for its rice an' corn, but for 'lass-es New Aw-leans.

SPEAKY, SPIKY SPOKY

Male Voices

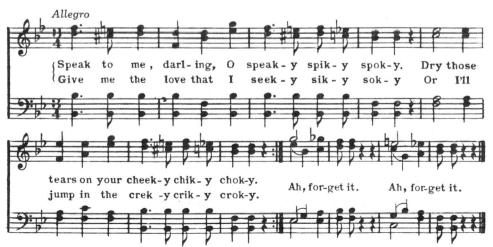

Allegro

{ Speak to me, darl-ing, O speak-y spik-y spok-y. Dry those
{ Give me the love that I seek-y sik-y sok-y Or I'll

tears on your cheek-y chik-y chok-y. Ah, for-get it. Ah, for-get it.
jump in the crek-y crik-y crok-y.

WE MEET AGAIN TONIGHT

Let Melody Flow

Male Voices

Song of Fellowship

We Meet Again Tonight

night, my boys. We'll laugh and sing and mer - ry be, and

night. With nev-er a sor - row near, boys,

mer - ry be to - night. We'll mer - ry be.

nev - er a fall - ing tear. We'll mer - ry be.

After 2nd verse

Slowly

Wel - come the time, my boys, we meet a - gain.

RED RIVER VALLEY

Male Voices

N. E. PEARSON

Slowly

1. { From this val - ley they say you are go - ing, I shall
{ I've been think-ing a long time, my dar - ling, Of the

2. { I have prom-ised you, dar - ling, that nev - er Shall the
{ When you think of the val - ley you're leav - ing, Oh! how

Red River Valley

miss your sweet face and your smile, (your smile); Just be-cause you are wea-
sweet words you nev - er would say, (would say); Now, a - las, must the fond
words from my lips cause you pain, (cause you pain) And my life it shall be
lone - ly and drear it would be, (it would be,) When you think of the fond

ry and tir - ed, You are chang-ing your range for a - while.
hopes all van - ish? For they say you are go - ing a - way.
yours for - ev - er, If you on - ly love me a - gain.
heart you're break-ing, And the pain you are caus - ing to me.

REFRAIN

Then come sit here a while ere you leave us; Do not

a - dieu

hast - en to bid us a - dieu; Just re mem-ber the Red Riv - er

a - dieu

Val - ley, And the cow - boy who loved you so true.

BRING THE WAGON HOME, JOHN
Male Voices

Oh, bring the wa-gon home, John. It will not hold us all. We

used to ride a-round in it When you and I were small. Oh,

used to ride a-round in it When you and I were small.

GOOD-NIGHT, LADIES
MALE VOICES

Slowly

1. Good - night, la - dies! Good - night, la - dies! Good - night, la - dies! We're
2. Fare - well, la - dies! Fare - well, la - dies! Fare - well, la - dies! We're
3. Sweet dreams, la - dies! Sweet dreams, la - dies! Sweet dreams, la - dies! We're

going to leave you now. Mer - ri - ly we roll a - long, roll a - long,
going to leave you now. Mer - ri - ly we roll a - long, roll a - long,
going to leave you now. Mer - ri - ly we roll a - long, roll a - long,

roll a - long; Mer - ri - ly we roll a - long O - ver the dark blue sea.

HANDCART SONG

Music arranged by
FREDERICK BEESLEY

Allegretto

1. Ye Saints who dwell on Eu-rope's shore, Pre-pare your-selves, for man-y more, To
   For you must cross the rag-ing main Be - fore the prom-ised land you gain, And

leave be-hind your na - tive land, For sure God's judg-ments are at hand.
with the faith-ful make a start, To cross the plains with your hand-cart.

CHORUS

For some must push and some must pull, As we go march-ing up the hill; So

mer-ri-ly on the way we go Un - til we reach the val - ley, O!

2.
As on the roads the carts are pulled,
'Twould very much surprise the world
To see the old and feeble dame
Thus lend a hand to pull the same!

3.
And maidens fair will dance and sing,
Young men more happy than a king;
And children, too, will laugh and play,
Their strength increasing day by day.

(Chorus)

DADDY, I'M A MORMON

Moderato

The Mor-mon fa - ther loves to see His Mor-mon fam-ily all a-gree With prat-tling chil-dren on each knee, Say-ing,

CHORUS

"Dad-dy, I'm a Mor-mon." Hey the mer-ry, ho the mer-ry, Hey the hap-py Mor-mon. I nev-er knew what joy was 'Till I be - came a Mor - mon.

ECHO CANYON

JAMES KIRKHAM

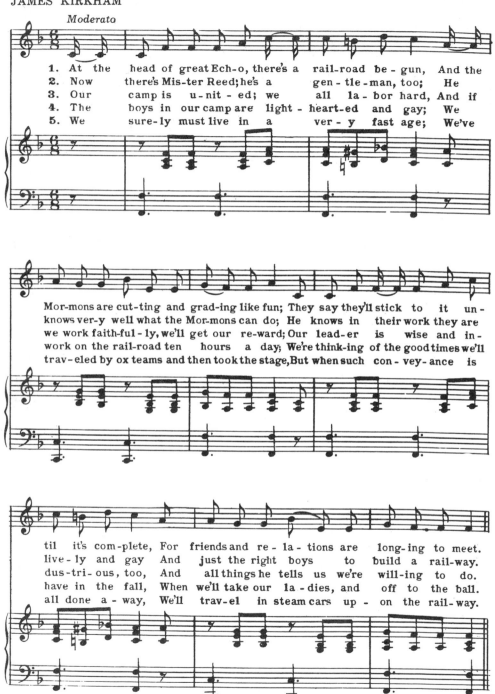

Moderato

1. At the head of great Ech-o, there's a rail-road be-gun, And the
2. Now there's Mis-ter Reed; he's a gen-tle-man, too; He
3. Our camp is u-nit-ed; we all la-bor hard, And if
4. The boys in our camp are light-heart-ed and gay; We
5. We sure-ly must live in a ver-y fast age; We've

Mor-mons are cut-ting and grad-ing like fun; They say they'll stick to it un-
knows ver-y well what the Mor-mons can do; He knows in their work they are
we work faith-ful-ly, we'll get our re-ward; Our lead-er is wise and in-
work on the rail-road ten hours a day; We're think-ing of the good times we'll
trav-eled by ox teams and then took the stage, But when such con-vey-ance is

til it's com-plete, For friends and re-la-tions are long-ing to meet.
live-ly and gay And just the right boys to build a rail-way.
dus-tri-ous, too, And all things he tells us we're will-ing to do.
have in the fall, When we'll take our la-dies, and off to the ball.
all done a-way, We'll trav-el in steam cars up-on the rail-way.

Echo Canyon

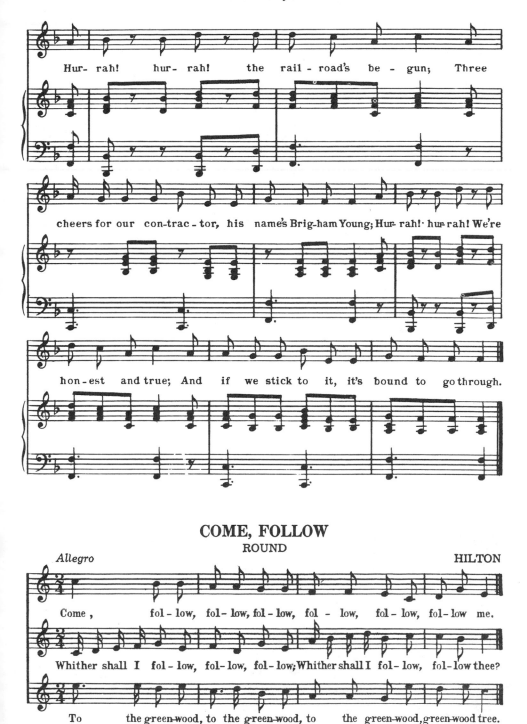

Hur- rah! hur- rah! the rail- road's be- gun; Three cheers for our con-trac - tor, his name's Brig-ham Young; Hur- rah!· hur-rah! We're hon - est and true; And if we stick to it, it's bound to go through.

COME, FOLLOW
ROUND

Allegro

HILTON

Come , fol - low, fol- low, fol- low, fol - low, fol - low, fol- low me.

Whither shall I fol - low, fol- low, fol- low; Whither shall I fol - low, fol- low thee?

To the green-wood, to the green-wood, to the green-wood, green-wood tree.

ONCE I LIVED IN COTTONWOOD

GEORGE A. HICKS

Folk Song

Moderato

1. Oh, once I lived in "Cot-ton-wood," And owned a lit-tle farm, But
2. I yoked old Jim and Bal-ly up, All for to make a start; To
3. At length we reached the "Black Ridge," Where I broke my wag-on down; I
4. While Bet-sy was a walk-ing, I told her to take care; When

I was called to "Dix - ie," Which gave me much a - larm; To
leave my house and gar - den It al-most broke my heart; We
could not find a car - pen-ter; We were twen-ty miles from town; So
all up on a sud - den, She struck a prick-ly pear; Then

raise the cane and cot - ton, I right a - way must go, But the
moved a - long quite slow - ly And oft - en looked be-hind, For the
with a clum-sy ce - dar pole, I fixed an awk-ward slide; My
she be - gan to blub - ber out As loud as she could bawl; If

rea - son why they sent me, I'm sure I do not know.
sands and rocks of "Dix - ie" Kept run - ning thru my mind.
wag - on pulled so heav - y then That Bet - sy could-not ride.
I was back in "Cot - ton - wood," I would-n't come at all.

Once I Lived In Cottonwood

5. And when we reached the Sandy, we could not move at all,
   For poor old Jim and Bally began to puff and lawl.
   I whipped and swore a little, but could not make them rout
   For myself, the team and Betsy, were all of us give out.

6. And next we got to Washington, where we stayed a little while
   To see if April showers would make the verdure smile.
   But Oh, I was mistaken, and so I went away,
   For the red hills of November, looked just the same in May.

7. I feel so sad and lonely now; there's nothing here to cheer,
   Except prophetic sermons, which we very often hear.
   They will hand them out by dozens, and prove them by the Book;
   I'd rather have some roasting ears; to stay at home and cook.

8. I feel so weak and hungry now; I think I'm nearly dead;
   'Tis seven weeks next Sunday, since I have tasted bread.
   Of carrot tops and lucerne greens we have enough to eat,
   But I'd like to change my diet off for buckwheat cakes and meat.

9. I brought this old coat with me, about two years ago,
   And how I'll get another one, I'm sure I do not know.
   May providence protect me against th ewind and wet.
   I think myself and Betsy, these times will ne'er forget.

10. My shirt is dyed with wild dockroot, with grease wood for a set;
    I fear the colors all will fade when once it does get wet.
    They said we could raise madder, and indigo so blue
    But that turned out a humbug; the story was not true.

11. The hot winds whirl around me, and take away my breath;
    I've had the chills and fever, till I'm nearly shook to death.
    "All earthly tribulations, are but a moment here."
    And oh, if I prove faithful, a righteous crown shall wear.

12. My wagon's sold for sorghum seed, to make a little bread,
    And poor old Jim and Bally, long, long ago are dead.
    There's only me and Betsy left to hoe the cotton tree;
    May Heaven help the Dixieite wherever he may be.

JOHN JOHNSON'S ARMY

Allegretto

You look-a to the East, And you look-a to the West, And you see John John-son a com-in', Four black mules and a pack a dern fools, and they land-ed on the oth-er side of Jor-dan. Let us be on hand with Brig-ham Young to stand, And if our en-e-mies do ap-pear, We'll sweep them from the land.

CARRY ON

RUTH MAY FOX

ALFRED M. DURHAM

Alla marziale e con spirito

1. Firm as the moun-tains a round us, Stal-wart and brave we stand, On the
2. We'll build on the rock they plant-ed A pal-ace to the King; In -

rock our fath - ers plant-ed For us in this good-ly land, The
to its shin - ing cor - ri-dors, Our songs of praise we'll bring, For the

rock of hon-or and vir-tue, Of faith in the liv - ing God. They
her - i - tage they left us, Not of gold or of world-ly wealth, But a

Carry On

Carry On

on, car - ry on, car - ry on. Hold - ing a - loft our

on, on, on. Hold - ing our

col - ors we march in the glo - rious dawn. O

col - ors we march in the glo - rious dawn. O

Carry On

youth of the no - ble birth-right, Car - ry on, car - ry on, car - ry

youth of the no - ble birth-right, Car - ry on, on,

rit. e cresc.

on.

on. Car - ry on, car-ry on, car - ry on. Car - ry on.

Carry On

Carry On

3 Trumpets in B♭

CHORUS

rit. cresc.

290

AS WE HOLD OUR BANNERS HIGH

Words and Music by
W. O. ROBINSON

1. In the west toward the land of the sun-set, Where the sky's ev - er smil - ing
2. In your col - ors we find in - spi - ra-tion, For the green is the strength of

fair, Where the snow caps with white ev - 'ry rock rug - ged height, And the
youth, And we'll stray not a - far while from sun-shine and star Gleams the

pines breathe their fra - grance rare There the skies glow with gold of the
gold, hea-ven's light of truth. And the trees stand-ing guard by the

As We Hold Our Banners High

sun - light, And the trees catch the hea - ven - ly ray Blaz - ing

road- side, Like true sen - ti - nels on our glad way. Ban - ners

forth green and gold, em-blems fair to be-hold Of the glo-ry of M. I. A.

fair, now they fling Gold and Green, while we sing Of the glo-ry of M. I. A.

CHORUS

Yes! M. I. A. we love you, And your mes-sage ev - er true. We

As We Hold Our Banners High

thrill a - new with glad-ness, As to - day we sing of you. Your

col - ors we will cher - ish; May they nev - er fade or die; Oh,

Gold and Green, of you proud - ly we sing, As we hold your ban-ners high.

COMRADES IN THE M. I. A.

Words and Music by
GENE BERGSTROM

Oh see that ban - ner gai - ly wav - ing
For us the sun is al - ways shin - ing,

In the skies of blue. It is the call to which we
For we're in the right. The clouds all have a sil - ver

Comrades In The M.I.A.

ral - ly; To it we'll be true. The M. I.
lin - ing, Ra-diant in the light. If you would

A. will lead us on - ward, Bring-ing joys un -
march with us to glo - ry, Join our M. I.

told. Let's all cheer to-geth-er for the
A. And all share the joy-ous life that's

Comrades In The M. I. A.

Green and Gold.
ours to - day.

We are the com - rades of the M. I.

A. Our col - ors Green and Gold;

We will al-ways work to-geth - er As friend ships true un -

Comrades In The M. I. A.

fold . Our high i - deals will be the guid-ing light That

leads us on our way, For we're all

com - rades in the M. I. A.

M. I. A. OUR M. I. A.

BERTHA A. KLEINMAN

1. Come, hail the cause of Zi-on's youth, M. I. A., our M. I. A. Come, hail her code of ev-'ry truth, M. I. A., our M. I. A. God's bless-ings on each ward and stake. Let praise re-sound; let song a-wake In ev-'ry heart that helps to make M. I. A., our M. I. A.

2. Be-neath her en-sign brave and free, M. I. A., our M. I. A. A loy-al band is proud to be, M. I. A., our M. I. A. As on and on and ev-er on, Where ser-vice calls us we be-long While God's ap-prov-al smiles up-on M. I. A., our M. I. A.

3. 'Mid hills and plains ninety thousand strong, M. I. A., our M. I. A. Come, push the might-y work a-long, M. I. A., our M. I. A. O Thou Su-preme o'er worlds a-far, 'Tis thou who guides our top-most star; O praise be thine for all we are, M. I. A., our M. I. A.

The following verses by another author may also be sung to the above music.

1. This is the work we love the best,
   M.I.A., our M.I.A.
   To thee we'll cling and stand the test,
   M.I.A., our M.I.A.
   There is no doubt about its fame,
   And proud we are of its great name;
   We'll always work to prove the same,
   M.I.A., our M.I.A.

2. So louder now we swell the strain,
   M.I.A., our M.I.A.
   Inspire our hearts thy heights to gain.
   M.I.A., our M.I.A.
   Let truth and honor be our goal;
   Exalt the life—make sweet the soul,
   And ever on the chorus roll,
   M.I.A., our M.I.A.

M. I. A., WE HAIL THEE

RUTH MAY FOX

W. O. ROBINSON

1. M. I. A., we hail thee! Loud thy praise we sing; For thy lov-ing guid-ance
2. Flow-er of the des-ert, Fra-grant is thy bloom, Blest with God's own sun-shine

We our hom-age bring; Found-ed by a proph-et On the rock of truth,
Ra-diant as the moon; 'Neath thy heav'n wrought ban-ner, March the brave and free,

CHORUS

May thy light and glo-ry Di - a - dem our youth. Ev - er, ev-er
For thy right-eous stan-dards, Hail, all hail, to thee! On,

On-ward, press on,

way

on - ward, God shall light thy way, light thy way;
on, ev - er on-ward God shall light thy way; yes,

on, on-ward. God light thy way, thy way; yes,

Glor - ious is thy prom - ise, Be-lov-ed M. I. A., M. I. A.
Glor-ious thy name, Glor-ious thy promise, M. I. A.

Glor-ious thy name, and prom-ise, Be-lov-ed M. I. A.

THE CLARION CALL

OSCAR A. KIRKHAM
Intro.

ALEXANDER SCHREINER

Trumpets in B (Flat)

Trumpets

Voices

The clar-ion call is sound-ing; The youth of Zion are march-ing; The voice of the Lord is heard; Each loy-al heart is stirred. For-ward we march;

The Clarion Call

For-ward we march, For-ward with ban-ners fly-ing!

Gold and Green, Gold and Green,The rays of the morn-ing greet you; A

hun-dred thou-sand cheer you; With cour-age a-new to live, to do, M. I.

A., we are march-ing; True to the faith we are march-ing.

WE WILL SING AS WE GO

CAROL H. CANNON   TRACY Y. CANNON

1. Life is a jour-ney of won-drous dreams, O'er moun-tains high, by
2. Friend-ships will blos-som where-'er we go In sum-mer's warmth, or
3. Ser - vice will lead us to rich - es rare, Up gold - en heights, through

spark-ling streams, Beck - on - ing ev - er to you and me.
win - ter's snow, Cheer-ing our lives as we jour - ney on.
val - leys fair, Bring-ing new joy to our hap - py hearts.

Come, let us take to the trail.
Come, let us take to the trail.
Come, let us take to the trail.

We Will Sing As We Go

AS THE ROSE

Two part Song

CLARISSA A. BEESLEY

EMERY G. EPPERSON

Moderato M.M. ♩ = 60 (2 slow beats to the measure)　Opus 156

Like the ros - es un - fold - ing at dawn Is our
Like the fra - grance of ros - es at eve Is the

youth with its ro-mance and dream-ing, With its laugh-ter and danc-ing and
sweet-ness and glad-ness of giv - ing, For the love that we give we re-

song, With its hopes like bright stars ev - er gleam - ing. As the
ceive, And the shar-ing makes life worth the liv - ing; AS THE

As The Rose

pet-als are shin-ing with dew, So may faith ev-er shine thru life's
ROSE thru the fair sum-mer days Sheds its per-fume, life's good-ness con-

sto - ry; With our eyes lift-ed up to the blue May our
fess - ing; So we, in our youth, sing our praise To the

path - way lead on to his glo - ry.
GIV - ER of good for his bless - ing.

rall. *rit.*

REFRAIN

Spirited M.M. ♩.= 80 (A little faster in 2)

Sing! Sing for the glad, gold-en hours Bring-ing their work and their pleas-ure,

As The Rose

Giv-ing us friend-ships so rare and so true, Home and the loved ones we treas-ure. Thanks! Thanks for the joys that are ours, For the strength and the cour-age of youth. All the world is a vi-sion be - fore us, Life filled with beau-ty and truth.

rall.

(short hold)

JUNIORS OF M. I. A.

ANGELYN W. WADLEY

MARK NICHOLS

Juniors Of M. I. A.

love and serve and nev - er swerve, From paths of truth and right; And ev-er

loy'l to our Jun-ior class are we. True Jun-iors we will ev - er be, And

al - ways we'll be guid-ed by the truths we learn to - day; We're

Jun-iors of M. I. A. Jun-iors of M. I. A. We'll join our

Juniors Of M.I.A.

hands and pledge our hearts and minds to M. I. A.

JUNIOR HIKING SONG

Words and Music by
ANGELYN W. WADLEY

Arranged by
MARK NICHOLS

Allegro

Sum-mer is here; it's a glo-rious day, Jun-ior girls of M I A. A-
Flow-er cups still hold the morn-ing dew, For-ests call to me and you; A-

way to the moun-tains we'll go, we'll go, Hik-ing, hik-ing, hi-ho. It's
way to the moun-tains we'll go, we'll go, Hik-ing, hik-ing, hi-ho. Oh,

Junior Hiking Song

time to get start-ed; the sun is high, Birds sing from ev-'ry tree. ヰ
may-be we'll come to a wa-ter-fall; May-be we'll see a squirrel. A

Flow-ers are bloom-ing on ev-'ry side; A trail is beck-on-ing me. We'll
deer or a fawn would de-light us all; So come ev-'ry Jun-ior girl. ヰ

fol-low a-long where cool breez-es blow, Jun-ior girls of M. I. A. A-
High to the hills where the clear streams flow, Jun-ior girls of M. I. A. A-

way to the moun-tains we'll go, we'll go, Hik-ing hik-ing, hi-ho.
way to the moun-tains we'll go, we'll go, Hik-ing hik-ing, hi-ho.

SPINNING SONG

CARL REINECKE

1. Spin, las - sie, spin; The thread goes out and
2. Sing, las - sie, sing, A mer - ry heart to
3. Learn, las - sie, learn; Good for - tune thus to
4. Smile, las - sie, smile; And turn your wheel the

in; Grow - ing as your tress - es grow,
bring; While the gold - en flax you spin,
earn; Learn to work and learn to play,
while; As the thread of life you spin,

Wis - dom with each year will show; Spin, las - sie,
Keep a cheer - ful heart with - in. Sing, las - sie,
Spin - ning on from day, to day. Learn, las - sie,
Weave the smile and song there - in; Smile, las - sie,

spin ; Spin , las - sie, spin.
sing ; Sing , las - sie, sing.
learn ; Learn, las - sie, learn.
smile ; Smile, las - sie, smile.

BEE HIVE JOYS

RUTH MAY FOX

ALFRED M. DURHAM

Sopranos may sing "Ah" for first four measures, or the words if preferred.

Bee Hive Joys

THE HONEY GATHERER'S SONG

TRACY Y. CANNON

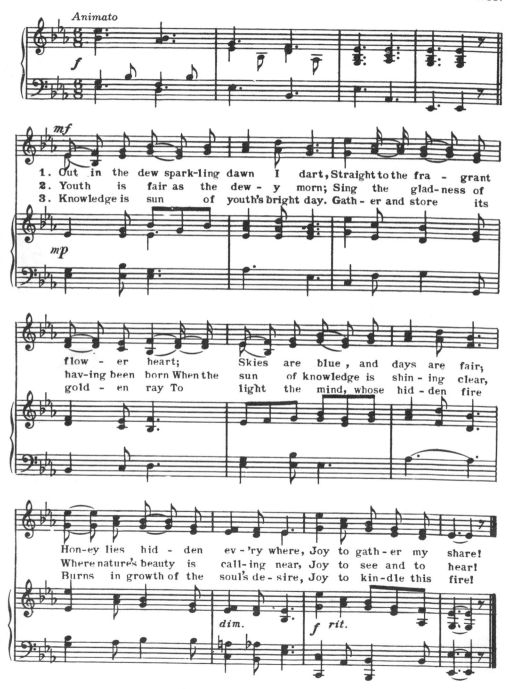

OH, THE BEE HIVE GIRLS ARE HIKING

Arr. by OSCAR KIRKHAM

Oh, the Bee Hive Girls are hik-ing, With our eyes on ev-'ry-thing. We will note each sound, ev-'ry track up-on the ground, And the clear cool spring and the bird up-on the wing. Oh, the Bee Hive Girls are hik-ing, And our col-ors are un-furled; And at ev-'ry turn we find something new to learn, Bee Hive Girls.

SONG OF JOY

MARY H. WOOLSEY

ROLAND C. PARRY

What does a bee do all day long? Gath-er the gold-en hon-ey

Hum-ming her lit - tle, hap-py song, All thru the day-time sun-ny.

Joy's in the task; Joy's in the task; May we

nev-er, nev-er, nev-er be done, With gath-er-ing gold-en hon-ey.

WHEN THE TWILIGHT SHADOWS FALL

OSCAR A. KIRKHAM

Music arr. from Old German
by OSCAR A. KIRKHAM

1. When the twi-light shad-ows fall And the lone loon's call-ing,
2. Now the night is draw-ing near; Cheer-ful fires are light-ed;

Then we know that night is near With its charm en-thrall-ing,
Bee Hive Girls from far and near, Loy-al hearts u-nit-ed.

And the sil-ver stars ap-pear, As the jew'ls of heav-en,
And for friends that we have made, Now a prayer to heav-en,

Then the Bee Hive Girls will sing. Hark! You hear us call-ing.
And a-gain we join in song. Hark! You hear us call-ing.

Then the Bee Hive Girls will sing. Hark! You hear us call-ing
And a-gain we join in song. Hark! You hear us call-ing

Wo-man-ho! Wo-man-ho! Wo-man-ho!

Note: The Womanho call may be used at the beginning as well as the end of the song if desired

THE SPIRIT OF THE HIVE

ZELLA A. JOHNSON

EDNA H. CORAY

Joyously

Gai-ly we wake with the glow-ing dawn, Hap-py to work till our
The faith of our fa-thers our guide shall be, The knowledge of truth that
For oth-ers our time will we free-ly give, Work-ing and help-ing while

task is done. Our ar-mor of faith we have gird-ed on, And
shall make us free. Ev-er we're striv-ing the light to see.
we may live. Self-ish-ness, sloth-ful-ness, and greed we drive

The Spirit Of The Hive

up-ward we climb till the goal is won.
Bus-y and hap-py to - day are we. *Humming*
Out and a - way from our hap-py hive.

With faith and knowledge, health and wom-an-hood, Beau-ty and work and truth We taste the sweet-ness of ser - vice, And

The Spirit Of The Hive

feel the joy of youth. We taste the sweet-ness of

ser - vice And feel the joy of youth.

cresc.

poco rit.

THE WOMANHO CALL

Lively

TRACY Y. CANNON

Wom-an-ho for Work! Wom-an-ho for Home! Wom-an-ho for Ser-vice to

all Man-kind, Wom-an-ho, Wom-an-ho, Wom-an-ho.

HELLO BEE HIVE

1. Hel - lo, Bee Hive, you're a friend of mine; Hel - lo, Bee Hive,
2. Hel - lo, Bee Hive, you're a friend of mine; Hel - lo, Bee Hive,

you're a friend of mine, With your jol - ly get to - geth - er, With your
you're a friend of mine, With your good times of the year, And your

glad and hap - py cheer. Hel - lo, Bee Hive, you're a friend of
mer - ry com - ra - dier. Hel - lo, Bee Hive, you're a friend of

mine, And I'll wave a - loft your ban - ner.
mine; You will keep my vis - ions bright - er.

BEE HIVE ROUND

The Bee Hive call a - ring - ing, Comes o - ver hills and lakes;

A - ring - ing, a - ring - ing, The clear sweet ech - o breaks:

Build - ers, Gath - 'rers, Guard - ians, feel joy.

THE M MEN ARE LEADING ALONG

1. O - ver hill, o - ver vale, ev - er on the up-ward trail, Lo! the
2. Proud ar - ray, day by day, Swell the ranks of M. I. A. And the

M Men are lead-ing a - long. On and on, might-y throng, Zi-on's
M Men are lead-ing a - long. On they press, strain or stress, Ev-'ry

men, ten thou-sand strong, Lo! the M Men are lead-ing a - long.
step for might - i - ness, Lo! the M Men are lead-ing a - long.

REFRAIN

Then it's M. I. A. in the van guard of the fray;

The M Men Are Leading Along

M Men of Zi - on, lift your song. The na - tions know where-
ev - er you may go, That the M Men are lead-ing a - long (keep them
(spoken)
lead-ing) That the M Men are lead-ing a - long.

RALLY SONG

HELENA W. LARSON   WILLIAM F. HANSON

We   meet   to - geth - er
We   keep   the stand - ards

Rally Song

Rally Song

Girls, M Men and Glean-er Girls.

GLEANER GIRLS AND M MEN

EMERY G. EPPERSON

Spirited

Glean-er Girls and M Men, Light the torch and "car-ry on". M. I. A. will rule then and will

Gleaner Girls And "M" Men

Gleaner Girls And "M" Men

Gleaner Girls And "M" Men

march straight a-head with eyes wide o - pen, Fac - es lift - ed to - ward the
sky, We will keep our vows from be - ing brok-en, And we'll
ev - er keep our stand - ards high. We have high.

YOUTH'S CALL

ELSIE C. CARROLL

WILLIAM F. HANSON

1. We are the youth of a West-ern emp-ire, Five hun-dred thous-and strong; We car-ry our ban-ner proud-ly, Lift-ed a-bove the throng. We stand for the cause of our fa-thers,

2. As our par-ents with faith and cour-age Did God's work with zest, So we, as the heirs they cher-ish, Take from their lives the best, And car-ry still on-ward their stand-ards

Youth's Call

God's ev - er - last - ing plan. We bear the torch in our
High in our eag - er hands. From youth to youth we will

on - ward march, The truth to the sons of man.
spread God's truth To the ends of his dis - tant lands.

rit.

CHORUS

a little slower

Right is the might we hon - or, Strength gained from pur - i -

ty, Cour - age to stand in a wav-'ring land And

Youth's Call

GOLDEN GLEANER'S PRAYER

GWEN and JAMES McCONKIE

1. O Lord, as we go forth to glean And bind our knowledge in - to sheaves, Pre-pare our hearts that we may find Great joy in serv-ing all man - kind. Give us the faith to la - bor long That we may bind the choic-est grains And bring to-ge - ther from the field The boun-teous har-vest thou didst yield.

2. We do not ask for less of toil, But on - ly for the strength to serve. We do not ask for sor-row's end, But by thy Spir-it com-fort lend. Help us, O Lord, to do the work That thou hast giv-en us this day. As Gold-en Glean-ers we would be Serv-ants of thine e - ter-nal - ly.

GOLDEN GLEANER THEME SONG

ANNABEA WAYMAN & JUDITH W. PARKER

JUDITH W. PARKER

1. Glean-ers gold, new and old, An-swer-ing the call,
2. Faith we bring as we sing Of the won-drous way.

Heights to gain, Friends at-tain, Joy for one and all.
Hea - ven's love From a - bove

guides us through the day. Hum _ _ _ _ Hap-pi - ness Comes to us,

Hum _ _ _ _ _ _
While we seek the truth, As we climb to heights sub-lime,

Golden Gleaner Theme Song

Hum _ _ _ _ _ _ _ _ _   In the steps of Ruth.

SING, GLAD HEART

(Two-part song for Women's Voices)

VILATE RAILE   FLORENCE JEPPERSON MADSEN

1. Sing out, Sing out, glad heart! Each
2. Sing out, Sing out, glad heart! Each
3. Sing out, Sing out, glad heart! Give

bright new day is mine, a Glean-er's, to make
ris-ing sun brings hope that I may earn, "Well
thanks for time, twice blessed, be-cause while yet it's

*The introduction should be played only before the first verse and should have the effect of trumpet calls.

Sing, Glad Heart

AROUND THE CAMPFIRE

OSCAR A. KIRKHAM

Oh, set the camp-fires burn-ing; Let's sit a - round the blaze. We'll
store some right good mem-'ries up To use in com - ing days, A
pict - ure of good com - rades With for - ces all a - light Who
sat be - neath the stars and sang A - round the camp - fire bright.

HIKING SONG

English hiking song

Alla marcia with gusto

1. Tramp, tramp, tramp, tramp, tramp, tramp, tramp, tramp,
2. Tramp, tramp, tramp, tramp, tramp, tramp, tramp, tramp,

I'm hap-py when I'm hik-ing, Pack up-on my back;
Out on the o-pen high-way, There's the place for me,

I'm hap-py when I'm hik-ing, Off the beat-en track,
High-road or dus-ty by-way, Lead-ing to the sea,

Out in the o-pen coun-try, Tramp-ing all the way, With a
Up hill or down the val-ley, Along some wind-ing lane, At the

Hiking Song

right good friend, To the jour-ney's end; Ten, twen-ty, thir-ty, for-ty, fif-ty miles a

break of day, Sing-ing on our way; Hap-py to be a-live and on the road a-

day. Tramp, tramp, tramp, tramp, tramp, tramp, tramp, Tramp! Tramp! Tramp!

gain. Tramp, tramp, tramp, tramp, tramp, tramp, tramp, Tramp! Tramp! Tramp!

Used by permission of Mr Max T. Krone
and the Niel A. Kjos Music Co.
Chicago

SCOUTING WE WILL GO

OSCAR A. KIRKHAM

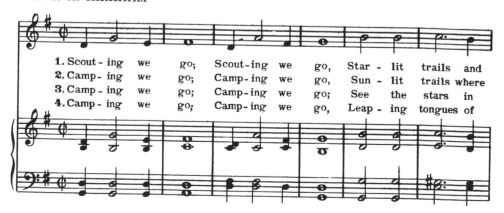

1. Scout-ing we go; Scout-ing we go, Star-lit trails and
2. Camp-ing we go; Camp-ing we go, Sun-lit trails where
3. Camp-ing we go; Camp-ing we go; See the stars in
4. Camp-ing we go; Camp-ing we go, Leap-ing tongues of

Scouting We Go

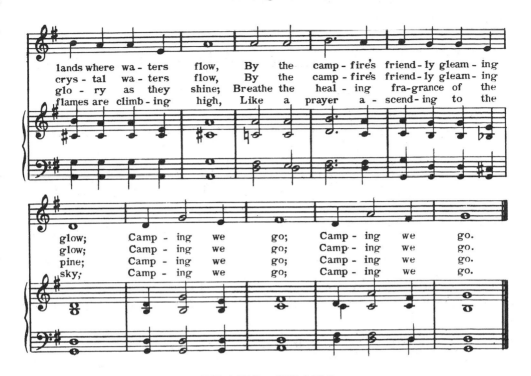

lands where wa - ters flow, By the camp - fire's friend - ly gleam - ing
crys - tal wa - ters flow, By the camp - fire's friend - ly gleam - ing
glo - ry as they shine; Breathe the heal - ing fra - grance of the
flames are climb - ing high, Like a prayer a - scend - ing to the

glow; Camp - ing we go; Camp - ing we go.
glow; Camp - ing we go; Camp - ing we go.
pine; Camp - ing we go; Camp - ing we go.
sky; Camp - ing we go; Camp - ing we go.

BRAVO—BRAVO

(International Scout Song)

Han skal le - ve, Han skal le - ve, Han skal le - ve.

Bra - vo, Bra - vo, Bra - vo, Bra - vis - si - mo, Bra - vo, Bra - vo,

Bra - vis - si - mo. Han skal le - ve, Han skal le - ve, Han skal le - ve.

EXPLORER HIKING SONG

OSCAR A. KIRKHAM

Hike on, hike on, ye val-iant men, Ex-plor-ers bold and free; We're march-ing a-way to meet a glor-ious new day; So let our hearts be light and free. Hike on, hike on, ye val-iant men, Ex-plor-ers bold and free, For we'll dare and

do and be ev-er true; On, Ex-plor-ers, Hike on, hike on!

EXPLORER HIKING SONG

For Male Voices

OSCAR A. KIRKHAM

Hike on, hike on, ye val-iant men, Ex-plor-ers bold and free; We're march-ing a-way to meet a glor-ious new day; So let our hearts be light and free. Hike on, hike on, ye val-iant men, Ex-plor-ers bold and free, For we'll

rit.

dare and do and be ev - er true; On, Ex - plor - ers, Hike on, hike on!

WE'RE ON THE UPWARD TRAIL

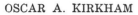

OSCAR A. KIRKHAM

We're on the up-ward trail; We're on the up-ward trail, Sing-ing as we

go, Scout - ing bound. We're on the up-ward trail; We're on the up-ward

trail, sing - ing, sing - ing, Ev' - ry - bod - y sing - ing, Scout - ing bound.

CLASSIFIED INDEX

ALPHABETICAL INDEX